Our world and its atoms

6

Photo on title page   A shower of lilac sparks from the metal potassium as it reacts violently with water.

The Open University, Walton Hall, Milton Keynes MK7 6AA

First published 1998. Reprinted 2000, 2001, 2002

Written, edited, designed and typeset by the Open University.

Printed and bound in Singapore under the supervision of MRM Graphics Ltd, Winslow, Bucks

ISBN 0 7492 8192 8

This text forms part of an Open University course, S103 *Discovering Science*. The complete list of texts that make up this course can be found on the back cover. Details of this and other Open University courses can be obtained from the Course Reservations and Sales Centre, PO Box 724, The Open University, Milton Keynes MK7 6ZS, United Kingdom: tel. (00 44) 1908 653231.

For availability of this or other course components, contact Open University Worldwide Ltd, The Berrill Building, Walton Hall, Milton Keynes MK7 6AA, United Kingdom: tel. (00 44) 1908 858585, fax (00 44) 1908 858787, e-mail ouwenq@open.ac.uk. Alternatively, much useful course information can be obtained from the Open University's website http://www.open.ac.uk

s103block6i1.4

Contents

1 Introduction

The main theme of the first half of *Discovering Science* is 'taking the world apart', and we embarked on it in Block 3 after the introduction to science provided by Blocks 1 and 2. In Block 3, we began by looking at the composition of the Universe, before settling on the tiny fragment that we know as the Earth. Then you saw how the Earth, in its turn, could be usefully taken apart into components such as the crust, the mantle and the core. In Block 4, we began to apply a similar process to the living things on the Earth, before the need to introduce the concept of energy in Block 5 called a temporary halt to it.

Now in Block 6 we return to the 'taking apart' theme with a vengeance. Up till now, the process of division has not taken us much below the level of what we can see with the naked eye, or with a microscope. Now we shall move into the invisible world of tiny atoms and molecules. To understand this world, you must study a scientific theory so important that it reaches into all parts of the course. This is the *atomic theory*, the idea that everything is made of atoms, of which there are about 100 different types.

The atomic theory provides the language of the makers of modern medicines and genetic engineers. Without an understanding of atoms we would not have lasers or an accurate value for the age of the Earth. The atomic theory is so important that the authors of previous blocks have not been able to keep their greedy hands off it, and you have already been introduced to a few atoms and molecules! In this block, however, we shall explore *scientific reasons* for believing in this atomic and molecular world.

One reason for believing is that, by using modern techniques, scientists can actually move individual atoms around like the bits of a jigsaw (Figure 1.1). But images like this are the output of a complex chain of electronics, computers and abstract theory, which is very hard to understand. Here in Block 6, we justify the existence of atoms by much more accessible experiments. Science can then be presented to you as it should be: not just as a body of knowledge, but as a *process* in which people think hard about experimental results, and what happens in the world around them. That thinking leads to the formulation of new theories about how the world works, and the theories are then tested and improved by designing and doing new experiments. In *Discovering Science*, Block 6 in particular has been designed to promote this message. It shows you how the interaction of thought and experiment first prompts us to propose the existence of atoms, then carries us to estimates of their mass and size, and finally leads to a belief that the atoms can themselves be taken apart into smaller bits.

The branch of science in which we shall mainly be working is called chemistry, and Sections 2–6 develop the idea that the world consists of about 100 chemical elements, each with its own distinctive type of atom. In Sections 7–10, the masses of these different types of atom are compared, and used to find out more precisely how one chemical element differs in its behaviour from another. In Section 12, we discover a pattern in those differences in behaviour, and build from it the Periodic Table of the elements.

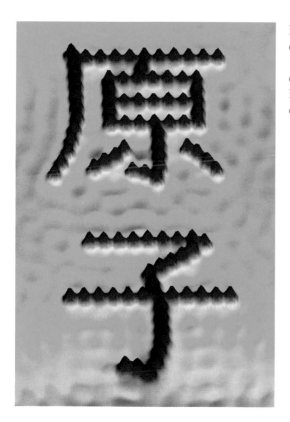

Figure 1.1 'Writing' with atoms: by using the technique called scanning tunnelling microscopy, the kanji characters for 'atom' have been written by arranging atoms of iron on a copper surface. You have already met another such image in Block 2, Figure 6.8. (Kanji is Japanese writing using Chinese characters.)

Up till Section 12, the world is regarded as a collection of atoms. Next, in Sections 13 and 14, experiments that use electricity and radioactive substances show that atoms themselves can be taken apart into particles called electrons, protons and neutrons. Such experiments also allow us to estimate the mass and size of individual atoms. The block then ends with a promise: the structure that we have begun to reveal within the atom itself will, later in the course, explain the Periodic Table of the elements.

The story that has just been outlined is logical, but it is also lengthy. So to help you keep hold of it, we have concentrated, in Block 6, on developing the skills of reviewing, and reflecting on, what you have learnt. In some cases, things for you to reflect on have been built into the summaries, and there are major reviewing activities, most notably in Sections 7, 10,and 15. The block also includes questions and activities on the design of experiments, and the use of the scientific method.

2 Doing chemistry

Many of the chemistry experiments on which we shall build our atomic theory bear obvious resemblances to cookery. One substance, for example, may be turned into another by mixing, dissolving, heating or cooling. As with cookery, there are particular problems for beginners: the ingredients sometimes have new and unfamiliar names, and so do the utensils. You will find some advice in the Study Guide that should help you to cope with the names of chemicals. In the case of the utensils, some help is provided in Box 2.1, *Chemical apparatus*. There is, however, nothing particularly unusual about the materials that we shall start with. They are all familiar, or they can be picked up somewhere on the Earth if you know where to look. What is important about them is that they can be used to make other, more spectacular substances which will both enlarge our experience, and advance our arguments. We begin on the Dorset cliffs.

Box 2.1 *Chemical apparatus*

We have provided you with three aids to help you get a feel for chemical apparatus. First, Plate 1 shows photographs of the more important items mentioned in Sections 2 and 3. Secondly, you will see many of these items in use in the video sequences. Thirdly, diagrams of the equipment used in particular experiments are often provided as line drawings. These are two-dimensional cross-sections of the apparatus (see Figure 2.1b).

(a)   (b)   (c)

Figure 2.1 (a) An artist's drawing of an airtight connection made between a narrow glass tube and a test-tube using a cork with a hole through it. (b) A line drawing of Figure 2.1a. (c) The same airtight connection made by using items with modern engineered glass joints.

The apparatus used in this block is a mixture of old and new. The older type uses connections made from rubber stoppers or corks (Figures 2.1a and b). The advantage of this type of apparatus is that it is relatively cheap, and learners sometimes have the means to put it together themselves. On the other hand, we also want to give you a flavour of a modern chemical laboratory. Here connections are made using machined ground-glass joints. In Figure 2.1c, the glass tube carries a tapered joint of this type, which fits snugly into a tapered socket in the neck of the test-tube.

2.1 The Lyme volcano: iron pyrite

It happened at Lyme Regis on 21 January 1908, and the news spread very quickly: there was an active volcano to the east of the town. There, on the cliffs whose tranquil beauty is extolled by Jane Austen in her novel, *Persuasion*, foul-smelling fumes rose from a huge cone of earth that had been formed in a recent landslip (Figure 2.2). On 24 January, the *Bridport News* carried a report on the 'volcanic eruption'. All spring

Plate 1 Some items of chemical apparatus that feature in Sections 2 and 3, and in the video sequences for Block 6. (a) A beaker, with a glass rod dipping into its contents, rests on a gauze square supported by a tripod; a burner beneath the gauze heats the beaker and its contents. (b) From the left: porcelain boat; porcelain crucible; glass filter funnel fitted with filter paper. (c) A desiccator with a blue drying agent; inside, orange crystals on a watch-glass are being dried. The watch-glass stands on a gauze sheet over the drying agent. (d) Test-tube rack with test-tubes. (e) From the left: round-bottomed flask with a ground-glass neck joint and fitted stopper; watch-glass with crystals; gas jar with air-tight greased cover slip.

Figure 2.2 The 'volcano' of 1908 on the cliffs at Lyme.

Figure 2.3 Crystals of the mineral pyrite, also known as 'fools' gold', often occur naturally with this characteristic cubic form.

Figure 2.4 The mineral melanterite, on the surface of a sample of weathered pyrite.

and summer, the smoke continued, and tourists arrived in large numbers. Down the coast at Charmouth, jealous traders hinted darkly that the Lyme folk were keeping the whole show going with occasional doses of paraffin. Only in the autumn did the volcanic activity subside.

The truth was less sensational but just as interesting. The cliffs at Lyme contain pebbles of the mineral pyrite, also known as iron pyrite or 'fools' gold' (Figure 2.3). When a landslip suddenly exposes the pyrite to air and rain, weathering (Block 2, Section 8.6) can begin in earnest. The heat that is generated in the process occasionally causes the pyrite to catch fire. On the Dorset coast, this is all the more likely because the mineral is embedded in shales that contain combustible tars. The smoke was the sign not of a volcanic eruption, but of **chemical reactions**.

You have already met some chemical reactions in this course. For example, in Block 2 (Section 6.4), you learnt how carbon will burn in air to give carbon dioxide. This process begins with carbon, a black solid, in the presence of oxygen, a colourless gas in the air. As the reaction proceeds, these two materials react together and the carbon disappears, along with some of the surrounding oxygen gas. As this happens, a new substance is produced; it is the colourless gas carbon dioxide.

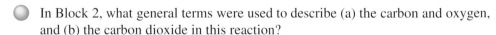 In Block 2, what general terms were used to describe (a) the carbon and oxygen, and (b) the carbon dioxide in this reaction?

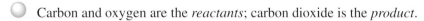 Carbon and oxygen are the *reactants*; carbon dioxide is the *product*.

In the reaction that took place at Lyme, the reactants were pyrite, which often occurs as golden-yellow pebbles, oxygen in the air, and rainwater. What the products are depends on the conditions, but if the process occurs much more slowly than it did at Lyme, and the products are not washed away, beautiful green crystals of the mineral melanterite (Figure 2.4) may appear on the surface of the pyrite. Another product is the gas sulfur dioxide, and this explains the smelly fumes.

Table 2.1 summarizes the reactants and products in the two reactions that we have discussed. It reveals things that are also true of many other chemical reactions. They are often marked by drastic changes of both form and colour. In the pyrite reaction, for example, the combination of a golden-yellow solid, a colourless, odourless gas and a colourless liquid is replaced by solid green crystals and a pungent-smelling, colourless gas. Again, chemical reactions are often accompanied by the evolution of heat — in this case, the 'volcano' occurred because of the heat generated during the reaction.

Table 2.1   Reactants and products for two chemical reactions.

Reactants	Products
Reaction 1	
carbon (a black solid)	carbon dioxide (a colourless gas)
oxygen (a colourless gas)	
Reaction 2	
pyrite (a golden-yellow solid)	melanterite (a green solid)
oxygen (a colourless gas)	sulfur dioxide (a colourless gas)
water (a colourless liquid)	

Now, what happens in nature can be done deliberately by people. Suppose we collect pyrite pebbles and allow them to weather in the open air for a long time. Melanterite forms on the surface of the pebbles. Pyrite resembles sand in that it does not dissolve in water, whereas melanterite resembles sugar and salt in that it does. We can use this fact to separate the two minerals (Figure 2.5). This figure introduces you to the important techniques of **dissolving** and **filtration** and also to the **evaporation** of a liquid (in this case water) with a view to obtaining a solid which has dissolved in it. In Britain during the 17th and 18th centuries, there was an industry which, ignoring one or two refinements, produced melanterite by just this method. The cliffs at Lyme were just one of the places from which the necessary pyrite was obtained. But the melanterite was not produced as an end in itself; it was used to make another chemical of much greater importance.

Figure 2.5   Making pure melanterite from weathered pyrite with melanterite on its surface by (a) dissolution, (b) filtration and (c) evaporation.

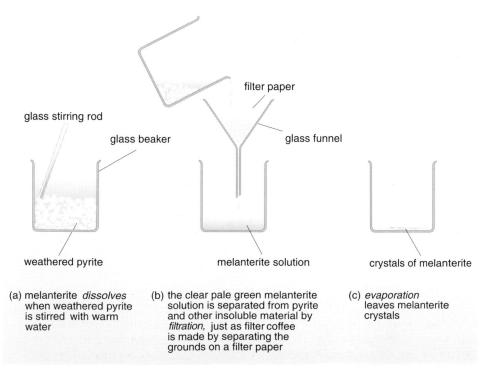

glass stirring rod

glass beaker

filter paper

glass funnel

weathered pyrite

melanterite solution

crystals of melanterite

(a) melanterite *dissolves* when weathered pyrite is stirred with warm water

(b) the clear pale green melanterite solution is separated from pyrite and other insoluble material by *filtration*, just as filter coffee is made by separating the grounds on a filter paper

(c) *evaporation* leaves melanterite crystals

2.1.1 Sulfuric acid

Suppose melanterite is placed in a sloping test-tube fitted with a cork that has a hole through its centre (Figure 2.6). A narrow glass tube fits snugly into the hole, and then descends to the bottom of a second test-tube where its tip is covered by a little water. The melanterite is heated by a flame, at first gently, and then much more strongly. It first turns white and then brown. At the same time, steam and other fumes appear above it and pass down the tubing into the water. The steam condenses, thereby increasing the volume of the water, and some of the fumes then dissolve in this liquid.

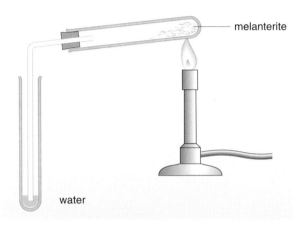

melanterite

water

Figure 2.6 Heating melanterite so as to collect an important product of the reaction that ensues.

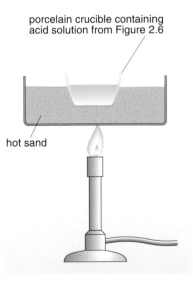

porcelain crucible containing acid solution from Figure 2.6

hot sand

Figure 2.7 Making concentrated sulfuric acid from the liquid produced in Figure 2.6. If the crucible is half-buried in hot sand, evaporation occurs gradually without splashing.

The liquid is now poured into a porcelain crucible (Plate 1b), half buried in sand and heated above 100 °C, the boiling temperature of water (Figure 2.7). Its volume decreases as steam and other fumes evaporate from it. Eventually a small amount of a dense, colourless oily liquid remains. This substance, once called oil of vitriol, is concentrated sulfuric acid. In the 17th and early 18th centuries, English sulfuric acid, made by using these particular chemical reactions, was exported to many parts of Europe.

Concentrated sulfuric acid is one of the most important industrial chemicals; in 1995, world production was about 200 million tonnes. It burns flesh (of which more later) and quickly turns sugar into charcoal. It absorbs water vigorously, and is therefore a useful drying agent. When it takes up water much heat is generated. In due time, you can watch these reactions on video (Activity 2.1).

2.2 On the Bolivian frontier: sodium nitrate

Nitrates are chemicals that are used to make fertilizers and explosives. There is only one large, natural deposit of nitrates in the world. In the Atacama desert in northern Chile (Figure 2.8) there occurs a material called *caliche* (pronounced ka-leesh), which may contain as much as 50% of sodium nitrate. This is a white solid that looks rather like table salt. As you will see in Block 8, chemists can now make nitrates from the nitrogen gas in air, but in the 19th century they could not, so the political and economic importance of the South American deposit was immense. In 1879, Chile waged a war for the nitrate fields against both Bolivia and Peru, and won it. Two coastal provinces then changed hands. From Peru, Chile gained its northernmost province of Tarapaca; from Bolivia came Antofagasta immediately to the south. As a result, Bolivia lost access to the Pacific and became the only entirely land-locked nation on the American continent.

○ As much as 80% of caliche by mass may consist of solids that dissolve in water. Why then have they not been dissolved and washed away by rain?

○ Because they occur in a desert region; the ports of Iquique and Antofagasta have heavy rains only two to four times a century.

To obtain pure sodium nitrate, we must separate it from the other components of caliche. These are of two types: insoluble impurities such as clay and sand, and impurities such as common salt (sodium chloride) which, like sodium nitrate, dissolve in water.

○ What techniques can be used to separate the soluble and insoluble components of caliche?

○ Dissolving and filtration: when the caliche is stirred with water and filtered, as in steps (a) and (b) in Figure 2.5, the insoluble sand and clay are caught by the filter paper, and the clear liquid that comes through contains the dissolved solids.

Now we must separate the sodium nitrate from the *soluble* impurities. We use the fact that very hot water can dissolve a lot of sodium nitrate, but cold water cannot. By contrast, hot and cold water dissolve similar amounts of the other soluble impurities, such as salt. The complete separation technique is shown in Figure 2.9. A considerable amount of caliche is added to boiling water and stirred. While still very hot the mixture is filtered. This separates the clay and sand. The clear liquid that comes through contains lots of sodium nitrate plus dissolved impurities, such as salt. It is chilled in an ice–water bath. A moment ago, you were told that cold water can dissolve very little sodium nitrate. So as the liquid cools, the water cannot hold all of the dissolved sodium nitrate in solution, and it separates out as colourless crystals. This process is called **crystallization**. Because cold and hot water dissolve similar amounts of salt, the salt remains in the solution as it cools. Now, if the *cold* mixture of solid crystals and liquid is filtered, the filter paper catches the sodium nitrate alone. It is still damp with the solution that it was dissolved in, and this contains impurities.

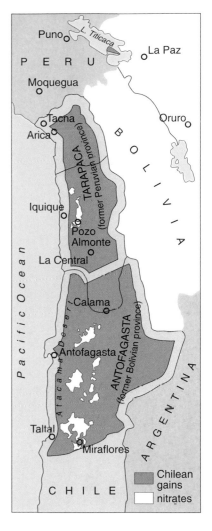

Figure 2.8 The proceeds of a war about a chemical. In 1879–1883, Chile won 'The War of the Pacific' against Peru and Bolivia for possession of the nitrate deposits in the northern Atacama desert.

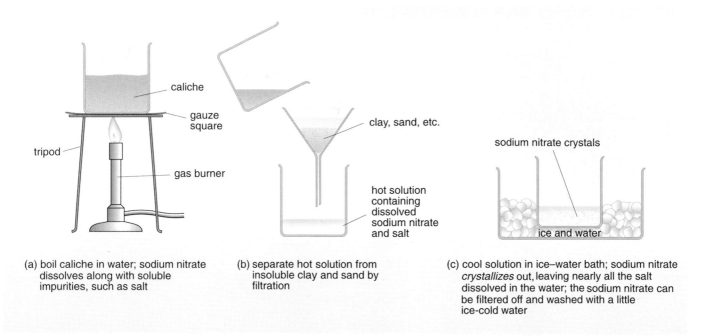

(a) boil caliche in water; sodium nitrate dissolves along with soluble impurities, such as salt

(b) separate hot solution from insoluble clay and sand by filtration

(c) cool solution in ice–water bath; sodium nitrate *crystallizes* out, leaving nearly all the salt dissolved in the water; the sodium nitrate can be filtered off and washed with a little ice-cold water

Figure 2.9 The extraction of sodium nitrate from caliche by crystallization.

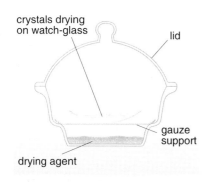

Figure 2.10 Solids that are still damp after they have been crystallized from water are often best left to dry out in a desiccator.

However, if a little ice-cold water is poured on to the crystals and allowed to drain through, the sodium nitrate is washed free of most impurities, and left damp largely with water alone. It can then be left to dry out in a **desiccator** (Figure 2.10 and Plate 1c): the solid, on a watch-glass (Plate 1e), is placed on a gauze platform above a chemical drying agent that absorbs water strongly. You will be asked to suggest possible drying agents later in Question 2.2.

In the Atacama desert, nearly one million tonnes of sodium nitrate are still extracted every year by using these principles. Most of it is consumed in fertilizers. We shall now use it in the way that we used melanterite: to make a rather more exciting substance.

2.2.1 Concentrated nitric acid

Figure 2.11 shows a glass container known as a retort. Today, a retort is seen more often in horror films than in chemical laboratories, but here it is ideal for our purpose. In it, we put some crystals of sodium nitrate, and then pour in an equal mass of concentrated sulfuric acid. We then carefully heat the mixture, and a reaction occurs. One of the products is called nitric acid. This is a liquid at room temperature. However, nitric acid has a much lower boiling temperature than sulfuric acid, and when the temperature reaches 80 °C, it begins to vaporize. The vapour passes into the cooler sloping neck of the retort where it condenses back to a liquid, and runs down into the flask, which is cooled by a flow of tapwater. This process of separation by vaporization followed by condensation is called **distillation**. If applied to fermented malted barley, it yields whisky!

The distillate that collects in the flask is slightly yellow because of impurities; when it is pure, nitric acid is colourless. Great care is needed when handling it. It attacks skin violently, staining it bright yellow, and you can say goodbye to any clothing that it is spilt on. Nitric acid dissolves most metals, including copper and silver, but not gold or platinum. You will see examples in Activities 2.1 and 6.2. Nitric acid is used

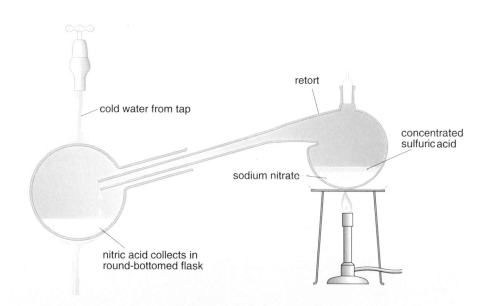

Figure 2.11 Using a retort to make concentrated nitric acid.

in the manufacture of all important military and industrial explosives. For example, the action of a mixture of nitric and sulfuric acids on cotton yields nitrocellulose. This also features in Activity 2.1.

Finally, let's consider the reactants and products of the reaction performed in this section. When all of the nitric acid has been distilled out of the retort in Figure 2.11, there remains only a white solid, which is different from the sodium nitrate that we started with. This new solid is called sodium hydrogen sulfate.

○ Name the reactants and products of the reaction performed in Figure 2.11.

○ We started with sodium nitrate and concentrated sulfuric acid; these are the reactants. As they are used up during the reaction, nitric acid and sodium hydrogen sulfate appear; these are the products.

So we can write: 'sodium nitrate *and* sulfuric acid *react to form* nitric acid *and* sodium hydrogen sulfate'. This statement can be more concisely represented by a **word reaction**. Where 'and' occurs in a statement, it is replaced by a plus sign; where 'react to form' occurs, it is replaced by an arrow that points *from* the reactants, which are consumed, and *towards* the products, which are formed. With these changes, the statement becomes:

sodium nitrate + sulfuric acid $\longrightarrow$ nitric acid + sodium hydrogen sulfate (2.1)

So to read a word reaction of this sort, you take the plus signs as 'and' and the arrow as 'react to form'.

2.3 The vanishing lake: sodium chloride

In many parts of the world, there exist vast deposits of common salt (sodium chloride, Figure 2.12) created by the evaporation of ancient seas. Each year, nearly 200 million tonnes are mined. Small amounts end up in salt cellars on dining tables; large amounts are used to make, among other things, soap, paper and plastics.

Figure 2.12 Crystals of the mineral halite or sodium chloride (common salt).

Mining on this scale leaves its mark. A dramatic example occurred in the US in 1980. An oil-drilling rig with a seven-man crew began explorations on Lake Peigneur in southern Louisiana. At 400 metres depth, the drill inadvertently holed the workings of the Jefferson Island salt mine, which lies beneath the lake. The lake promptly disappeared into the hole, grounding two fisherman in a flat-bottomed boat. Having disposed of Lake Peigneur, the hole now turned its attention to the Gulf of Mexico, drawing on a canal that linked the lake to the sea. By now the hole was marked by a 15 metre waterfall, and the fishermen decided on retreat. Waist deep in mud, they dragged their boat to shore, and tied it to a tree on the banks of the lake. As they hurried away across the now-trembling earth, they saw boat, tree and bank disappear into the muddy vortex. By the end of the day, the hole had also swallowed a tugboat, several barges and the $5 million oil rig.

Let's put this commonplace chemical, which is mined on such a huge scale, to use. From it, we shall make hydrogen chloride, a choking corrosive gas.

2.3.1 Hydrogen chloride and hydrochloric acid

Figure 2.13 shows how hydrogen chloride can be made. Concentrated sulfuric acid is dropped into a flask containing sodium chloride. This generates hydrogen chloride gas, which leaves the flask and bubbles through a bottle of concentrated sulfuric acid before collecting in the gas jar on the right (Plate 1e).

Figure 2.13 Making hydrogen chloride gas.

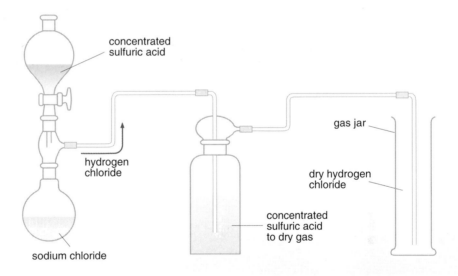

Now in Section 2.1.1, you were told that concentrated sulfuric acid absorbs water. Because of this, in Figure 2.13, it can fulfil two roles. It acts first as a *reactant* in the flask to the left; secondly, it acts as a *drying agent*, drying the hydrogen chloride gas as it bubbles through the bottle on the way to the gas jar.

Hydrogen chloride is a colourless gas that is *denser* than air. This explains the position of the tip of the delivery tube in the gas jar. That position enables the tube to carry the hydrogen chloride to the bottom of the gas jar, where its density encourages it to remain. It tends to stay in the jar, filling it up from the bottom. We say that hydrogen chloride is collected by *upward displacement of air*: as it accumulates, it pushes the air above it upwards and out of the jar.

At the upper boundary of the hydrogen chloride, where the gas makes contact with moisture in the air, fumes appear. These are droplets of hydrochloric acid, the result of hydrogen chloride dissolving in water. The very great solubility of hydrogen chloride in water is shown in Figure 2.14. It is also demonstrated in Activity 2.1.

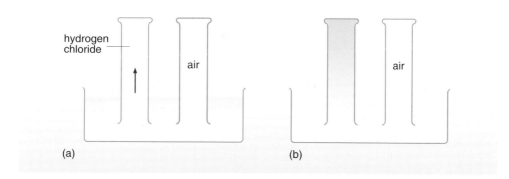

Figure 2.14 (a) Jars of air and hydrogen chloride are inverted over water. (b) The air stays put, but the hydrogen chloride is dissolved by the water, which rises and fills the jar.

At normal room temperature, one litre of water can dissolve as much as 450 litres of hydrogen chloride. The result is concentrated hydrochloric acid, a colourless, corrosive liquid. You will learn more about what it can do in the next section.

2.4   A first look at acids

The three substances that we ended up with in Sections 2.1.1, 2.2.1 and 2.3.1 were all called *acids*: sulfuric acid, nitric acid and hydrochloric acid. They are among the most important substances in any chemical laboratory, where they are usually found in two forms, both of which are solutions in water. The first is the *concentrated acid*; this contains the higher proportion of the parent substance (sulfuric acid, nitric acid or dissolved hydrogen chloride). For example, a kilogram of concentrated nitric acid contains about 0.7 kilogram of pure nitric acid and 0.3 kilogram of water. The second form is the *dilute acid*, which is much less corrosive and is made by adding lots of water to the concentrated form. For example, dilute nitric acid is made by adding about seven volumes of water to one volume of the concentrated acid.

What is it about the three chemicals that makes us call them acids? Here we shall respond to that question by showing you how the three acids, in their dilute forms, have the same effect on certain key substances.

2.4.1   The effect of acids on litmus

On cliffs in the Canary Islands, there grows the lichen, *Roccella tinctoria*, from which a blue dye, litmus, can be extracted. Litmus can be dissolved in water or used to colour paper. Sulfuric, nitric and hydrochloric acid all turn its blue colour red. *Acids turn blue litmus red.*

2.4.2   The effect of acids on limestone

Limestone country with its ravines and cliffs, often on inland sites, such as Malham and Cheddar Gorge, is amongst the most beautiful in the British Isles. Limestone is just one form of the chemical substance, calcium carbonate. Others are chalk and marble. When calcium carbonate is added to one of our three acids, there is vigorous effervescence as a gas is produced (Figure 2.15). This gas is carbon dioxide, which is so important in the greenhouse effect (Block 2). *Acids react with limestone and give carbon dioxide.*

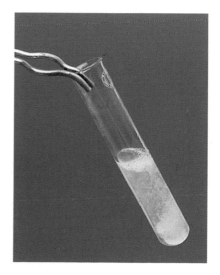

Figure 2.15 The action of an acid on calcium carbonate; carbon dioxide gas is produced.

Figure 2.16 shows how we can use this reaction to collect samples of carbon dioxide. Here, the particular acid that we use is hydrochloric, and the displaced carbon dioxide is first bubbled through water to remove any hydrogen chloride fumes that are carried over with it, i.e. to 'wash' the gas.

Figure 2.16 The reaction between calcium carbonate and hydrochloric acid can be used to make dry carbon dioxide.

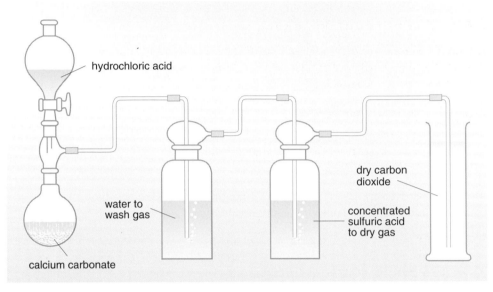

Why does this *remove* hydrogen chloride?

Hydrogen chloride is very soluble in water (Section 2.3.1). Carbon dioxide is only slightly soluble, and so is not removed.

The gas is then dried by concentrated sulfuric acid and collected in a gas jar.

What does the position of the delivery tube tip in the gas jar tell you about the properties of carbon dioxide?

The gas is denser than air; like hydrogen chloride (Figure 2.13), it is collected by upward displacement of air.

If enough hydrochloric acid is added, all of the calcium carbonate in the flask will react and dissolve in it, and when the reaction is over, a clear solution remains. If this liquid is poured into a porcelain crucible and heated, the remaining dilute hydrochloric acid will evaporate, leaving a white solid that was dissolved in the solution. This solid can then be heated more strongly to drive off any residual water. Then, to make sure it stays dry, it is cooled in a desiccator (Figure 2.10) and finally stored in a sealed jar. It is called calcium chloride and is most useful because it is an enthusiastic absorber of water vapour.

Name two products of the reaction between calcium carbonate and hydrochloric acid.

One is calcium chloride; another is carbon dioxide.

In fact there is a third, which is water. This is not easily proved here because it just augments the water of the dilute hydrochloric acid in the flask, and is not easily seen.

Now write down a word reaction for these changes, showing reactants and products.

calcium carbonate + hydrochloric acid ⟶ calcium chloride +
carbon dioxide + water   (2.2)

The reactants are separated by plus signs to the left of the arrow; the products are similarly separated to the right.

2.4.3 The effect of acids on magnesium

The familiar metals iron, tin and zinc react with acids to give a colourless gas. The less familiar metal magnesium also does this, but in a more lively fashion. Because magnesium has a low density, it is much used in airframes, luggage and spacecraft. More magnesium has been put into orbit than any other metal. When magnesium chippings are added to dilute hydrochloric or sulfuric acids, there is vigorous effervescence as the metal gradually reacts with, and dissolves in, the acid.* Figure 2.17 shows how the reaction can be carried out so as to collect the gas that is responsible for the effervescence.

How does the position of the gas jar differ from that shown in Figures 2.13 and 2.16? Can you suggest a reason for the difference?

The jar is now upside down, showing that the gas produced in the reaction must be less dense than air. The tube carries the incoming gas to the base of the jar which is now uppermost. The light gas accumulates, thereby filling the jar from the top down: the gas is collected by *downward displacement of air*.

The gas in question is called hydrogen. *Acids react with magnesium to give hydrogen.*

Many other metals, zinc for example, also liberate hydrogen from acids. Hydrogen has the lowest density of all known substances (Figure 2.18). It explodes if mixed with air in a confined space and ignited, and this property can be used as a test for the gas (Figure 2.19). When exposed to plenty of air it burns quietly when lit. Because of this flammability, hydrogen is no longer used as a lifting-gas for airships (Figure 2.20).

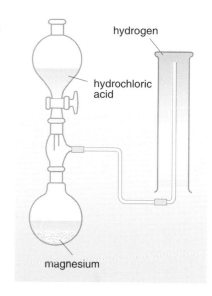

Figure 2.17 The reaction between magnesium chippings and hydrochloric acid produces a gas, which is collected as shown.

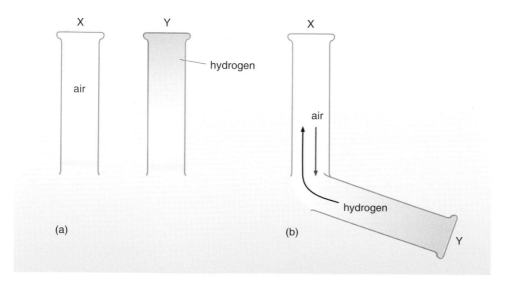

(a)   (b)

Figure 2.18 Hydrogen gas has a density only one-fifteenth that of air. It can therefore be poured upwards. In (a), the jar Y initially contains hydrogen; the jar X contains air. The upward pouring shown in (b) causes the hydrogen to move from Y to X, pushing the air in X downwards and out.

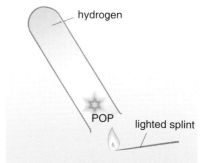

Figure 2.19 A simple laboratory test for hydrogen: the gas burns with a squeaky pop.

* The same reaction occurs with nitric acid, but only if the acid is *very* dilute. If this is not so, the reaction is of a different type.

Figure 2.20 The German airship *Hindenburg* was destroyed in 1937 when the hydrogen lifting-gas caught fire. Notice how the lightness of hydrogen drove the flame upwards; because of this there was a surprising number of survivors (62 out of a total complement of 97).

Activity 2.1   Introducing chemistry

During this activity you will see many of the reactions described in Section 2. Getting a feel for materials and equipment is an important part of science. Such knowledge is acquired not by reading, listening or doing written tests, but by watching and handling things. In this activity, all you need to do is watch! ◀

Activity 2.2   A glossary of chemicals

This activity gives you the chance to start your own glossary of chemicals that play an important part in the block.◀

2.5   Summary of Section 2

In Section 2, a number of chemical reactions were used to turn key starting materials into important new products. Reaction flow diagrams are a concise way of summarizing operations of this sort, and Figure 2.21 is an example. The arrows go from the key starting material to a key product, and alongside the arrow are written the operations and other reactants needed to initiate the reaction. For example, the step marked by the arrow pointing upwards from concentrated sulfuric acid tells us that when this acid is heated with sodium nitrate, concentrated nitric acid can be distilled off. Substances that will play an important part in the reasoning used in the block have been boxed.

To emphasize the importance of the boxed chemicals, we now summarize in words what Section 2 had to say about them.

1   Concentrated sulfuric acid absorbs water strongly and is therefore a good drying agent. When heated with sodium nitrate, it forms nitric acid; when heated with salt (sodium chloride), it yields hydrogen chloride gas, which dissolves very readily in water to give concentrated hydrochloric acid.

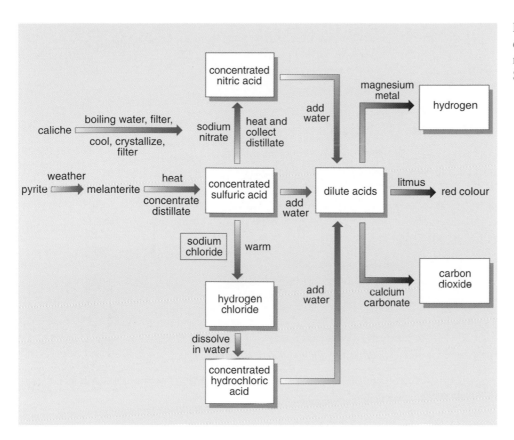

Figure 2.21 This reaction flow diagram summarizes the chemical reactions that you have studied in Section 2.

2   Concentrated sulfuric, nitric and hydrochloric acids are corrosive liquids, which quickly attack skin and clothing.

3   The dilute acids turn litmus red, react with calcium carbonate to give carbon dioxide, and with magnesium metal to give hydrogen. Hydrogen is a colourless flammable gas with a density much less than that of air; carbon dioxide is denser than air.

4   After calcium carbonate has dissolved in dilute hydrochloric acid, evaporation to dryness yields a white solid called calcium chloride, which is a very good drying agent.

Besides providing you with information, the text and the video activity have also introduced you to some chemical operations and equipment. These operations include dissolving, filtration, evaporation, distillation, crystallization and the collection of solids and gases. If you have understood their purpose, you should now be able to tackle some very simple problems of experimental design yourself (Questions 2.2–2.5).

Finally, think again about sulfuric, nitric and hydrochloric acids. These are three immensely important chemicals, and each year, world industry consumes many millions of tonnes of each one. In Section 2, they are made by methods that use simple equipment, but have obvious disadvantages. For example, the weathering of pyrite is a slow business that takes months, so it is best not to base sulfuric acid manufacture on it. Then again, it would be politically unwise to tie a national fertilizer and explosives industry to a single nitrate deposit on the west coast of South America. Can we therefore find better ways of making these valuable chemicals? The answer is that we can, if we come to a *scientific* understanding of what is going on. It is to this that we shall turn in Section 3.

Question 2.1   The preparation of hydrogen chloride is illustrated in Figure 2.13. When the chemical reaction has ended, the white solid that remains in the flask is the same as that left at the bottom of the glass retort of Figure 2.11 after the preparation of nitric acid. Write a word reaction for the preparation of hydrogen chloride, and identify the reactants and products. ◄

Question 2.2   Name two substances (liquid or solid), either of which might be put into the bottom of the desiccator in Figure 2.10. ◄

Question 2.3   The ship is sinking in mid-Pacific, no distress signal has been sent out, and you must take to the boats, which have only a limited supply of fresh water. The portable chemistry set that you always carry with you includes the following items: beaker, test-tubes, gas burner, filter funnel, filter papers, flask, retort, porcelain crucible, stirring rod. Which *two* items from this set would you choose to take with you, and why? ◄

Question 2.4   Explain how, by using the techniques of Section 2, you could separate a mixture of salt and sand, and end up with both substances in their solid forms. ◄

Question 2.5   In the preparation of carbon dioxide in Figure 2.16, the gas is bubbled through bottles containing water and sulfuric acid. Would the preparation be equally effective if the positions of the two bottles were exchanged, and the gas was bubbled first through sulfuric acid, and then through water? Explain your answer. ◄

Question 2.6   Vinegar turns blue litmus red. Predict two other chemical reactions that you would expect it to take part in. ◄

Doing chemistry quantitatively

So far we have just *watched* chemical reactions happen. Reactants have disappeared and been replaced by products, but you have been given no reason why, for example, hydrogen chloride and not gold is produced when salt is heated with sulfuric acid. To reach such understanding scientifically, we must *measure* things.

The sort of thing we want to know is how much of some particular product is formed from some particular amount of reactant: we want to know the *quantities* of substances. A good way of measuring quantities of substances is by mass. This is done by following the procedure used to measure out apples in the supermarket: the apples are put on the pan of an electronic balance, and the mass, in kilograms, is read off a digital display to three decimal places. A modern laboratory balance (Figure 3.1) is similar except that it is surrounded by a transparent case to exclude draughts, the mass is displayed in grams, rather than in kilograms,* and the reading is given to four decimal places rather than to three. Let's use this instrument to answer an important question.

3.1 Does the total mass change in a chemical reaction?

We begin with particular cases. Silver nitrate is a white solid similar in appearance to salt. Like salt, it also dissolves in water to give a clear colourless solution. Figure 3.2 shows how the reaction between this solution and dilute hydrochloric acid can be carried out, all within a corked flask. If the flask and its contents are carefully weighed both before and after the reaction, the mass is found to be unchanged. Thus in the case of this particular reaction, there is no detectable† change in mass.

Figure 3.1 A modern electronic laboratory balance, which can read to 0.000 1 g (0.1 mg). A balance like this contains a standard mass and a built-in program that can be used to reset the instrument should it be moved to a new site where the Earth's gravity might be slightly different.

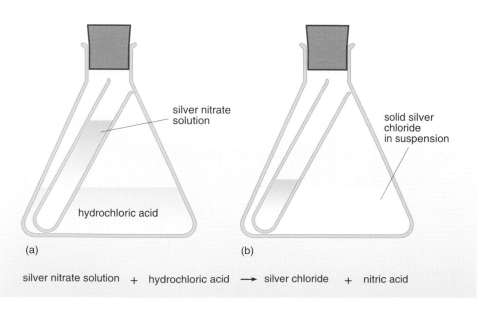

(a)   (b)

silver nitrate solution + hydrochloric acid ⟶ silver chloride + nitric acid

Figure 3.2 (a) A test-tube containing a clear colourless solution of silver nitrate stands in clear colourless dilute hydrochloric acid. If the flask is tilted to pour some of the silver nitrate solution into the acid, fine white particles of a **precipitate** of solid silver chloride immediately appear in the flask, (b). The word reaction at the bottom of the figure shows that the other product is nitric acid.

* When making measurements, scientists choose units of the most convenient size. In this block, masses are determined in grams and volumes in litres. These are more convenient than the units kg and m³ used in previous blocks.

† This means that the mass change cannot be detected by the balance shown in Figure 3.1 (i.e. any difference is less than 0.000 1 g).

This proposition has been tested by using many other kinds of chemical reaction, including reactions involving gases. For example, white phosphorus burns in air. A piece of white phosphorus is placed in a flask, which is then corked and weighed. The flask is now warmed until the phosphorus catches fire, covering the inside of the flask with a fine white solid product. When the reaction has stopped, the flask is allowed to cool and it is then reweighed. No detectable change in mass has occurred. Provided we perform the reactions in sealed containers, so that neither products nor reactants can leak out, other examples tell the same story. We therefore advance a general proposal called the **law of conservation of mass**:

During any chemical reaction, there is no detectable change in mass.

What does this tell you about the masses of the reactants and products?

As there is no overall mass change, the total mass of the reactants that are consumed must be equal to the total mass of the products that are formed.

We now put this idea to work.

3.2   Copper and copper oxide

Copper is a reddish-brown metal that everyone is familiar with. It is used in electrical wiring and some household utensils. If a piece of copper foil or wire is heated strongly in air, the surface turns black. This colour change does not happen if the heating is done in air from which oxygen has been removed: a chemical reaction has occurred in which copper and oxygen are the reactants and the product is a black powder. This black powder is called copper oxide.

Write a word reaction for this change.

copper + oxygen $\longrightarrow$ copper oxide   (3.1)

Let us investigate the reaction quantitatively. Masses (in grams) can be determined to four decimal places (Figure 3.1), but to simplify the arithmetic, we shall use masses determined to only three. A slim porcelain boat (Plate 1b) is carefully weighed; its mass is 11.613 g. Reddish, powdered metallic copper is now carefully added to it until the combined mass of boat and copper becomes 12.613 g: the change in mass tells us that we now have 1.000 g of copper in the boat. The boat is now heated in a stream of dry air or oxygen (Figure 3.3), and reaction 3.1 occurs.

Figure 3.3   A porcelain boat containing copper powder is heated in a stream of dry air or oxygen.

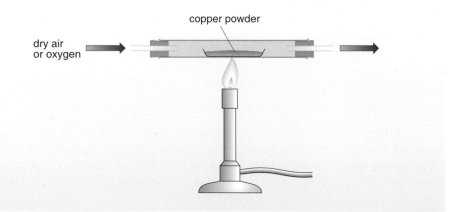

When the reaction begins, the mass of the boat and its contents increases as the copper takes up oxygen from the gas stream. The increase is very gradual because the reaction is slow, but eventually the mass increase stops. *All* of the reddish copper in the boat has now been converted into black copper oxide, and the final measurement can be made. The heating is stopped, and the boat is withdrawn and placed in a desiccator (Figure 2.10) to cool. It is then weighed, and the mass is found to be 12.865 g.

The results that we have just obtained are summarized in Table 3.1.

Table 3.1   The mass changes in an experiment of the type shown in Figure 3.3.

Before heating in oxygen

mass of porcelain boat	=	11.613 g
mass of porcelain boat + copper	=	12.613 g
mass of copper in boat	=	1.000 g

After heating in oxygen

mass of porcelain boat + copper oxide	=	12.865 g
mass of copper oxide in boat	=	1.252 g

○ Pencil in the missing figure against the mass of copper oxide at the bottom of the table.

○ You should have written 1.252 g, which is the mass of the boat plus copper oxide, less the mass of the boat.

We conclude, therefore, that when 1.000 g of copper is heated in oxygen, 1.252 g of copper oxide are formed.

○ Use the law of conservation of mass to deduce how much oxygen has combined with the 1.000 g of copper.

○ The mass of the product (1.252 g) must be equal to the mass of copper (1.000 g) plus the mass of oxygen that was taken up. So the mass of oxygen is (1.252 – 1.000) g = 0.252 g.

So far, what we have established is that 1.252 g of copper oxide are formed from 1.000 g of copper and 0.252 g of oxygen. But one further experiment will allow us to put this in a more revealing way. Suppose we put our boat with its copper oxide and total mass of 12.865 g into the apparatus shown in Figure 3.4. This allows the copper oxide to be heated in a stream of hydrogen gas. Quite quickly, another reaction occurs, and the black powder in the boat turns reddish-brown.

○ What do you think this reddish-brown substance is?

○ It is powdered metallic copper.

Even more striking is the result of weighing the cooled boat and copper when the reaction is over. Its mass turns out to be 12.613 g. As Table 3.1 shows, this is the mass that it had after we loaded it with copper at the start of these experiments. The 1.000 g of copper that we converted into copper oxide has now been totally recovered from that oxide by heating it in hydrogen. It is as if the copper never quite went away: it

Figure 3.4 How to heat the porcelain boat containing copper oxide in a stream of hydrogen gas. Before heating is started, hydrogen is passed through the tube for some time to flush out all air. Then the hydrogen stream can be ignited at the jet where air is plentiful without fear of explosion (see Section 2.4.3). Now the glass tube and boat can be heated to start the reaction.

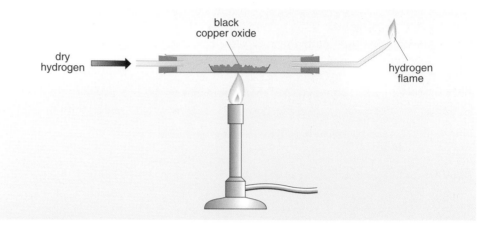

was still available to us in the copper oxide if we were clever enough to find out how to get it back. It is therefore tempting to argue that 1.252 g of copper oxide is not just *formed from* 1.000 g of copper and 0.252 g of oxygen; it *contains* 1.000 g of copper and 0.252 g of oxygen. Let us persevere with this kind of language and see where it takes us.

3.3 Copper oxide from copper and nitric acid

We mentioned in Section 3.2 that heating copper in air or oxygen is a slow and therefore inconvenient way of converting the metal into copper oxide. There is another way that begins by dissolving copper in nitric acid. This is sometimes called Remsen's reaction because of the dramatic description given by an American chemist of that name (see Box 3.1, *Remsen's reaction*).

Box 3.1 Remsen's reaction

Ira Remsen (Figure 3.5) has left us a striking description of the moment that decided his future career:

> While reading a textbook of chemistry, I came upon the statement, "nitric acid acts upon copper", and I determined to see what this meant. Having located some nitric acid, I had only to learn what the words "act upon" meant. In the interests of knowledge, I was even willing to sacrifice one of the few copper cents then in my possession. I put one of them on the table, opened the bottle marked "nitric acid", poured some of the liquid on the copper, and prepared to make an observation. But what was this wonderful thing which I beheld? The cent was already changed, and it was no small change either. A greenish-yellow liquid foamed and fumed over the cent and over the table. The air became coloured dark-red. How could I stop this? I tried by picking up the cent and throwing it out of the window. I learned another fact; nitric acid acts on fingers. The pain led to another unpremeditated experiment. I drew my hands across my trousers and discovered that nitric acid acts on trousers. This was the most impressive experiment I have ever performed. I tell of it even now with interest. It was a revelation to me. Plainly the only way to learn about such remarkable kinds of action is to see the results, to experiment, to work in a laboratory.

Figure 3.5 Ira Remsen (1846–1927).

From 1876 onwards, Remsen transformed the teaching of chemistry in the American universities by establishing laboratory-centred education. In 1878, he asked one of his assistants, Constantine Fahlberg, to try out some new reactions that he had thought up. When Fahlberg did this, he noticed that one of the products was extremely sweet, and he patented it as an artificial sweetener without telling Remsen. The new substance was saccharin, and Fahlberg later made a fortune. This did not please Remsen who was hostile to links between commerce and the academic world. He would not feel at home in the universities of today!

You can see Remsen's reaction in Activity 6.2. The red gas that appears is nitrogen dioxide. It is a poisonous irritant that gets mentioned in air quality forecasts. It is produced following a reaction between the nitrogen and oxygen in air at the high temperatures within car engines. Figure 3.6 shows a photograph that reveals nitrogen dioxide in Los Angeles smog.

Figure 3.6   A view towards central Los Angeles from the south showing the layer of pollutants over the city. The colour of the haze is due, in part, to nitrogen dioxide.

Here, our concern will be with what happens when we do Remsen's experiment quantitatively. As in Section 3.2 we begin with 1.000 g of copper powder, weighed this time into a porcelain crucible. Some dilute nitric acid is added, and the crucible is covered with a small watch-glass, leaving a small gap so that gases and vapour can escape. The copper powder dissolves in the acid, which turns green, and the red gas streams through the gap. When things quieten down, we heat the crucible gently (Figure 3.7). More red fumes appear, but they are not so intense, and as the liquid gets hot, it evaporates steadily. None of the liquid, which contains the dissolved copper, must splash out.

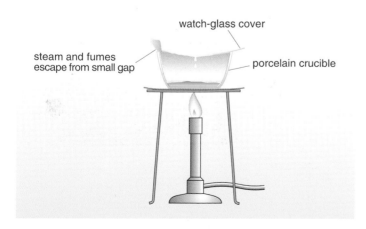

watch-glass cover

steam and fumes
escape from small gap

porcelain crucible

Figure 3.7   Avoiding the loss of dry or dissolved solids from the porcelain crucible when heating copper with nitric acid. Any splashes on the underside of the watch-glass are washed back by steam, which condenses and drips back into the liquid below.

Eventually, evaporation proceeds so far that blue-green crystals appear in the small amount of liquid left at the bottom of the crucible. These are crystals of copper nitrate. Further heating drives off all the remaining liquid. Now the heating is intensified, and as the temperature of the copper nitrate crystals increases, they begin to decompose. More fumes of nitrogen dioxide appear, and the blue-green crystals turn black. When the decomposition is over, the crucible is placed in a desiccator to cool, and then weighed. This weighing shows that the crucible contains 1.252 g of the black product.

The black substance thus obtained looks just like the copper oxide that was made by heating copper in oxygen in Section 3.2. It is also chemically similar: for example, both substances dissolve in dilute hydrochloric, sulfuric or nitric acid to give clear greenish-blue solutions, and both are converted back into copper when heated in a stream of hydrogen. Even more striking is the quantitative similarity revealed by the weighings. In Section 3.2, 1.000 g of copper combined with 0.252 g of oxygen to give 1.252 g of black copper oxide. In Section 3.3, we again began with 1.000 g of copper. After dissolving it in nitric acid, evaporating the solution and heating the blue-green crystals that result, we again obtained 1.252 g of a black powder. We conclude that both black powders are copper oxide, and that in both cases, a 1.252 g sample contains 1.000 g of copper and 0.252 g of oxygen.

This conclusion prompts a question. If copper oxide is made up of copper and oxygen, where did the oxygen come from when we made it by the reaction of copper with nitric acid? It did not come from the air, because we get the same result if the reaction is performed under air from which oxygen has been removed.

○ Can you suggest a source for the oxygen?

○ It must have come from the nitric acid.

And it does. Figure 3.8 shows an experiment that supports this belief. When nitric acid is heated by itself, it decomposes, and oxygen gas is one of the products. When it is heated with copper, the end result seems to be that some of this oxygen, instead of being lost to the atmosphere, is transferred to the copper, and copper oxide is thus formed.

Figure 3.8 Nitric acid contains oxygen. An old-fashioned clay pipe is clamped with the bowl upright, the stem tilted, and the mouthpiece under water. The submerged tip is covered by an inverted test-tube, completely filled with water, and then the stem is made red-hot. Nitric acid poured into the bowl decomposes in the hot stem and the products issue from the mouthpiece. All of them except oxygen are very soluble, and dissolve in the water, but the oxygen fills the test-tube by displacing the water. If the test-tube is removed, a glowing splint can be rekindled by the oxygen it contains.

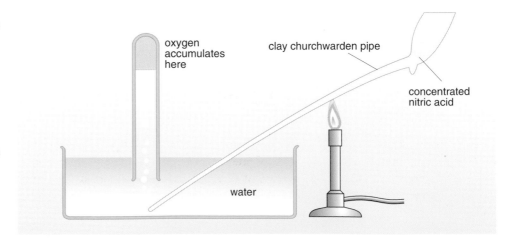

3.4   The concept of chemical composition

Although our two 1.252 g samples of copper oxide were prepared in different ways, they are both composed of 1.000 g of copper and 0.252 g of oxygen. There is, however, another way of representing this composition – by using percentages. Let's calculate the percentages of copper and oxygen in the 1.252 g samples of copper oxide:

$$\text{copper percentage} = \frac{\text{mass of copper}}{\text{mass of copper oxide}} \times 100\%$$

$$= \frac{1.000\,\text{g}}{1.252\,\text{g}} \times 100\% = 79.9\%$$

$$\text{oxygen percentage} = \frac{\text{mass of oxygen}}{\text{mass of copper oxide}} \times 100\%$$

$$= \frac{0.252\,\text{g}}{1.252\,\text{g}} \times 100\% = 20.1\%$$

Note that the sum of the two percentages is 100%, as it must be.

This composition, however, refers to samples obtained from 1.000 g of copper. Does the composition change when the mass of copper that we start with is different? You can answer this by doing Question 3.1.

Question 3.1   The answer comes from an experiment in which a mass of copper, different from 1.000 g, is completely converted into black copper oxide, either by the method of Section 3.2, or by that of Section 3.3. Table 3.2 shows the experimental results. Check that you can perform the essential calculations of Sections 3.2–3.4 by filling in the blank spaces in Table 3.2, and calculating the percentage composition of the copper oxide which is produced. How does the percentage composition compare with that found for the 1.252 g sample above.◄

Table 3.2   The data for an experiment of the type shown in Figure 3.3.

mass of boat	=	10.486 g
mass of boat and copper powder	=	11.986 g
mass of copper powder	=	1·500g
mass of boat and copper oxide	=	12.364 g
mass of copper oxide	=	1·878g

(handwritten annotations)

copper %age = $\dfrac{1.500g}{1.878g}$ = 79.9%

O₂ %age = $\dfrac{1.878g - 1.500g}{1.878g}$ = 20.1%

From Question 3.1, you should have found that the percentage compositions of the two samples are the same. This is most important. We have now made black copper oxide by different methods, and by starting with different masses of copper. In each case, its chemical composition has proved to be the same. If this is generally true, then:

A chemical substance with its distinctive properties — colour, melting temperature, chemical reactions — has a characteristic chemical composition.

For the moment, it will be enough to say that this composition lists the percentages, by mass, of the constituents that the compound contains. In the case of copper oxide, these constituents are copper and oxygen. We shall arrive at a more precise meaning of the word *constituent* in Section 4. But first, we shall use the composition of copper oxide to determine the chemical composition of a much more important compound.

3.5   Water

Water can be broken down into its constituents by passing an electric current through it. There is a slight difficulty: water is not a very good conductor of electricity. The difficulty, however, can be overcome by lacing the water with a few drops of sulfuric acid. This greatly improves the conductivity of the liquid, and an ordinary 9 volt radio battery will then do the job (Figure 3.9). Gas bubbles appear on the small pieces of metal foil where the electrical circuit makes contact with the liquid, and can be collected as shown. When a flame is applied to the gas obtained from the foil connected to the negative terminal of the battery, the gas burns with a squeaky pop. In other words, it has the characteristic explosive quality of hydrogen (Section 2.4.3), so we can assume that it *is* hydrogen. Likewise, the gas obtained from the foil connected to the positive terminal rekindles a glowing splint. This is a characteristic property of the gas oxygen: things burn in oxygen, and in pure oxygen, they are especially flammable. You see these tests for hydrogen and oxygen during Activities 2.1 and 6.2, respectively.

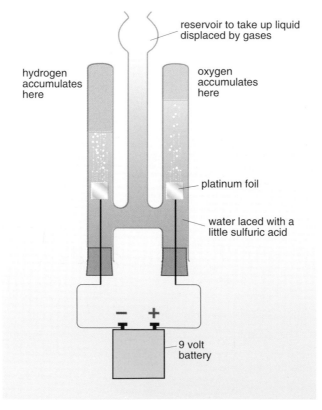

reservoir to take up liquid displaced by gases

hydrogen accumulates here

oxygen accumulates here

platinum foil

water laced with a little sulfuric acid

− +

9 volt battery

Figure 3.9   Decomposing water with electricity: small pieces of platinum foil are attached to the ends of wires fixed to the terminals of a 9 volt battery. Gases appear when the foils are immersed in water laced with sulfuric acid, and can be collected over water as shown. One gas, hydrogen, seems to have twice the volume of the other, oxygen. This can be ignored for now, but becomes important later.

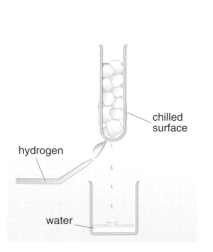

chilled surface

hydrogen

water

Figure 3.10   A small flame of hydrogen burning in air is played on a test-tube containing ice. The gaseous combustion product condenses on the cool surface and drips on to the watch-glass beneath. It boils at 100 °C and can be safely drunk: it is water.

Water, then, is decomposed into hydrogen and oxygen by an electric current. This suggests that water is composed of hydrogen and oxygen. To confirm this proposition, we simply reverse the process. You know that hydrogen burns in the oxygen of the air (Figures 2.19 and 2.20). Figure 3.10 shows how this process can be safely carried out, and how the product of the reaction can be collected. That product proves to be water. Water, then, is composed of hydrogen and oxygen, and when hydrogen burns in the oxygen of the air, the two constituents react, and water is formed:

$$\text{hydrogen} + \text{oxygen} \longrightarrow \text{water} \tag{3.2}$$

Thus when hydrogen is used as a fuel, the product is water vapour. From Block 2, you know that atmospheric water vapour is a greenhouse gas, but any influx from the burning of hydrogen should fall back to Earth as rain or snow. So using hydrogen as a fuel should not increase the amount of water vapour in the atmosphere, or cause global warming. This advantage has given rise to a vision of the future called 'the hydrogen economy' (Box 3.2, *Imagining the future: a hydrogen economy*).

Box 3.2 *Imagining the future: a hydrogen economy*

If and when the hydrogen economy arrives, then you will turn the tap on your gas cooker, and hydrogen will come out instead of natural gas. To refuel your car, hydrogen gas might be pumped into the fuel tank where special powdered metal alloys will react with it to form solid hydrides. When the car is up and running, these hydrides will be heated to release hydrogen gas, which can then be burnt in the engine instead of petrol. Then there will be no need to feel guilt about global warming: your exhaust emissions will consist of water vapour and contain no carbon dioxide. In the home,

hydrogen and oxygen might be continuously supplied to special devices called fuel cells in which the two gases react, and supply both your electricity requirements, and drinking water as well.

Hydrogen will be made by the decomposition of water, either electrically (Figure 3.9) or by some other method. So the whole thing is a water cycle, which is different from the one introduced in Blocks 1 and 2 in that it is kept going by people rather than by nature (Figure 3.11). But before we can enjoy this earthly paradise, vital problems must be solved. The biggest is the energy

source which keeps the whole cycle spinning. If carbon dioxide emissions are to be avoided, the electricity for the decomposition of the water must be provided without burning fossil fuels. Nuclear power is one solution, but this produces dangerous radioactive waste. Some progress has been made with devices called photoelectrosynthetic cells in which the electric current for the decomposition is produced by sunlight, but there is still a long way to go. At the moment, the hydrogen economy looks more a distant prospect than something which is just around the corner.

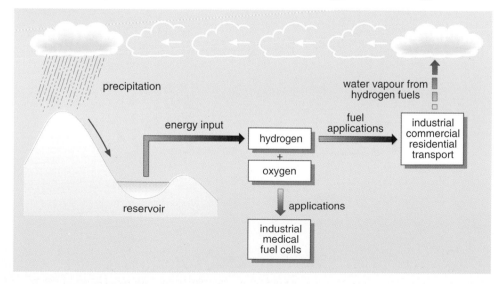

Figure 3.11 An artificial water cycle, which might describe a future hydrogen economy.

We can find the chemical composition of water by using the reaction pictured in Figure 3.4. There we found that, when copper oxide was heated in hydrogen, the hydrogen took up the oxygen in the copper oxide and left the copper behind; copper is one of two products in the reaction.

⬤ What do you think the other product is? Write a word reaction for the change.

◯ Because hydrogen reacted with the oxygen in the copper oxide, water is the likely product:

hydrogen + copper oxide ⟶ copper + water   (3.3)

Figure 3.12 shows how this reaction can be made to reveal the composition of water. A typical set of results is shown in Table 3.3.

Figure 3.12 Finding the composition of water: a boat containing copper oxide is heated in dry hydrogen. The water that is formed is carried as a gas to a U-tube containing calcium chloride. The calcium chloride is a drying agent (Section 2.4.2) and absorbs the water. When we stop heating, the increase in the mass of the calcium chloride tube tells us how much water has been formed; the decrease in the mass of the boat tells us the mass of oxygen that this mass of water contains. The chemical composition of water can then be calculated.

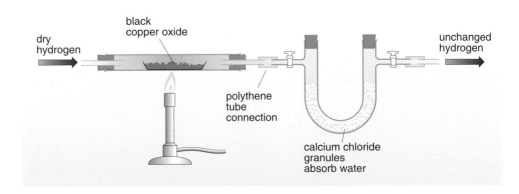

Table 3.3   The data for the experiment of Figure 3.12.

mass of calcium chloride tube before experiment	=	10.625 g
mass of calcium chloride tube after experiment	=	11.863 g
mass of water vapour formed	=	
mass of copper oxide boat before experiment	=	14.786 g
mass of copper oxide boat after experiment	=	13.687 g
mass of oxygen lost from the boat	=	

⬤ Pencil in the mass of water vapour that has been formed, and the mass of oxygen that it contains.

◯ The difference between the calcium chloride tube masses tells us that 1.238 g of water have been formed; the difference between the two boat masses tells us that this water contains 1.099 g of oxygen.

⬤ Now calculate the percentages of oxygen and hydrogen in water.

◯ The oxygen percentage is $\frac{1.099}{1.238} \times 100\%$ or 88.8%; the remaining 11.2% of the water must be hydrogen.

To summarize, the chemical composition of water by mass is 88.8% oxygen and 11.2% hydrogen.

Elements and compounds

4

We have now taken two substances, copper oxide and water, and shown that each of them can be taken apart into two constituents: copper oxide contains copper and oxygen; water contains hydrogen and oxygen. We proved this by careful measurements of masses, and the clever use of chemical reactions. But however clever we are, we find that we cannot take copper, hydrogen or oxygen apart in a similar way. Substances like this, which cannot be broken down by chemical reactions into simpler constituents, are called **chemical elements**. Substances like copper oxide and water, which can be so broken down and are therefore a chemical combination of chemical elements, are called **chemical compounds**. You first met these two terms in Block 2, Section 6.3.1. You will notice that when we gave you the chemical compositions of copper oxide and water as percentages of their 'constituents', those constituents were chemical elements. And this is what the **chemical composition** of a compound is: the masses of the constituent elements that a sample contains, expressed as percentages of the total mass of the sample.

Many millions of chemical compounds exist, but there are only about 100 chemical elements. Already in this course you have met quite a few of these elements: they include the colourless gases oxygen, hydrogen and nitrogen, the metal copper, and carbon, which usually occurs as a black solid. Table 4.1 lists the compounds that you have met in this block, alongside their constituent elements. New elements include sodium, calcium, chlorine and sulfur. Sodium and calcium are silvery metals, which react vigorously with water to give hydrogen gas. Chlorine is a choking poisonous yellow-green gas, which was employed in early gas attacks in the First World War, and is used to kill bacteria in water; sulfur is a yellow solid found on the slopes of volcanoes. Photographs of some chemical elements, including two that are liquid at room temperature, are shown in Figure 4.1.

Table 4.1 The constituent elements of all the chemical compounds that you have met so far in this block.

Compound	Constituent elements	Compound	Constituent elements
pyrite	iron, sulfur	calcium carbonate	calcium, carbon, oxygen
melanterite	iron, hydrogen, sulfur, oxygen	carbon dioxide	carbon, oxygen
sulfuric acid	hydrogen, sulfur, oxygen	calcium chloride	calcium, chlorine
sulfur dioxide	sulfur, oxygen	silver nitrate	silver, nitrogen, oxygen
sugar	carbon, hydrogen, oxygen	silver chloride	silver, chlorine
sodium nitrate	sodium, nitrogen, oxygen	copper oxide	copper, oxygen
nitric acid	hydrogen, nitrogen, oxygen	copper nitrate	copper, nitrogen, oxygen
sodium chloride	sodium, chlorine	water	hydrogen, oxygen
hydrogen chloride	hydrogen, chlorine		

Most of the chemical elements are **metals**, which are familiar from their lustrous, shiny appearance and the fact that they are good conductors of electricity. In Figure 4.1, metals are represented by aluminium, sodium, and mercury, a liquid metal. Solid **non-metals**, such as sulfur, usually have a matt appearance, and are poor electrical conductors; this is also true of the liquid non-metal bromine. Some non-metallic elements are gases, such as chlorine. A small number of the chemical elements have intermediate electrical conductivities and are called **semi-metals**, or semiconductors. Silicon is the best known example.

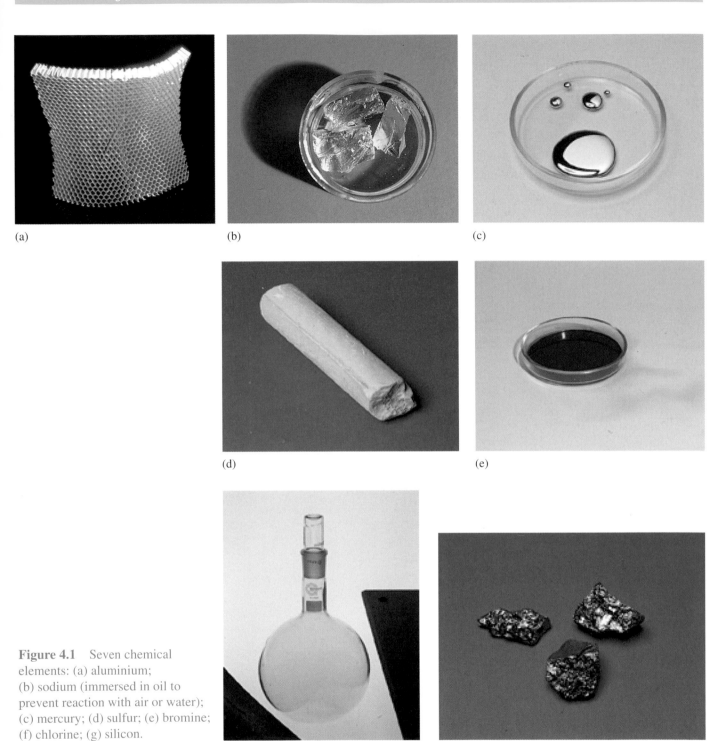

Figure 4.1 Seven chemical elements: (a) aluminium; (b) sodium (immersed in oil to prevent reaction with air or water); (c) mercury; (d) sulfur; (e) bromine; (f) chlorine; (g) silicon.

In Section 3.2, we recovered *all* the copper that we had turned into copper oxide by the reaction of that oxide with hydrogen. This suggests that the *amounts* of the chemical elements are unchanged in chemical reactions; they merely undergo a change in the elements with which they are combined. For example, when copper oxide reacts with hydrogen, the amount of oxygen is unchanged: it simply leaves the copper and combines with hydrogen.

In all chemical changes, chemical elements are neither created nor destroyed.

It is this that turns the distinction between chemical elements and chemical compounds into such a powerful idea.

We can show its power with some examples. So far in this block, chemistry has just been a question of throwing substances together and waiting. We have had no idea beforehand of what might be produced. For all we know, it might be possible to make sulfuric acid by heating limestone with salt. The concept of a chemical element tells us that this is impossible. Table 4.1 shows us that sulfuric acid is composed of the elements hydrogen, sulfur and oxygen. All three elements of which it is composed must therefore be present in any materials that we make it from. But Table 4.1 shows that neither limestone (calcium carbonate) nor salt (sodium chloride) contains sulfur. Therefore, it is pointless to try to make sulfuric acid in this way.

● Is it pointless to try to make sulfuric acid from sulfur, oxygen and water?

○ No it is not; between them, sulfur, oxygen and water contain the elements sulfur, hydrogen and oxygen, which are the constituents of sulfuric acid.

In fact, the modern process for making sulfuric acid starts from just these three substances. That process is a great deal more convenient and economical than allowing pyrite to weather, and heating the product. Thus the concept of a chemical element has pointed us towards the improvements that we were looking for at the end of Section 2. We are developing a scientific understanding of chemistry.

4.1 A first look at chemical symbols

The chemical elements are such an important part of modern science that each one is given a special symbol. This has been the case for many years: Figure 4.2 shows a set, devised in about 1800, which are combinations of letters and signs. Modern symbols consist simply of either one or two letters, the first letter being a capital. Some examples for elements that you have already met are shown in Table 4.2. Most symbols are obviously extracted from the modern names of the elements; thus O is oxygen, N is nitrogen and Cl is chlorine. Some, however, date from a time when Latin was the universal language of learned Europeans. Cu (copper), Hg (mercury) and Na (sodium) come from cuprum, hydragyrum and natrium, the Latin names of the three elements. You will become familiar with the symbols for the more important elements as you work through this block.

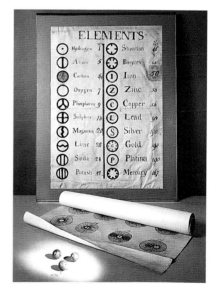

Figure 4.2   The set of symbols for the chemical elements that was used by John Dalton, of whom you will hear more in Section 6.

Table 4.2   Symbols for some chemical elements that you have met so far in this block.

Element	Symbol	Element	Symbol	Element	Symbol
aluminium	Al	copper	Cu	oxygen	O
bromine	Br	hydrogen	H	silver	Ag
calcium	Ca	iron	Fe	sodium	Na
carbon	C	mercury	Hg	sulfur	S
chlorine	Cl	nitrogen	N	zinc	Zn

Chemical symbols can have one of two meanings, depending on the context in which they are being used. Here we introduce you to the first meaning, in which they represent the chemical elements as *substances*. In this context, the capital letter S stands for the yellow solid that we call sulfur, and the symbol Cl for the yellow-green gas that we call chlorine. We shall meet the other meaning of chemical symbols in Section 6.1.

4.2 A first look at chemical names

The chemical names of compounds reveal the elements of which the compounds are composed. In this first look, we shall deal with some cases where the link is obvious. Copper oxide, for example, is composed of copper and oxygen. This is an example of a type of compound that you will meet frequently in this block. It is a **binary compound**: one composed of just two elements. In such a case, one element (copper) is written down first, and the other (oxygen) comes second, but with its name modified to end in -ide. Very often, such binary compounds are a combination of a metallic element, such as iron, silver or copper, with a non-metallic element such as oxygen, sulfur or chlorine. The name of the metallic element is then written first, and the modified name of the non-metallic element second (e.g. oxide, sulfide, chloride).

● What would be the name of a binary compound formed between sulfur and aluminium?

○ Aluminium sulfide; aluminium is a metal, and sulfur is a non-metal. The name of the metal is written first, and as this is a binary compound, the ending of the name of the non-metal is modified to -ide.

Table 4.1 also contains names similar to this, except that the second word ends not in -ide, but in -ate. In cases encountered in this course, the ending -ate indicates that the compound contains oxygen in addition to the two other named elements. Thus calcium carbonate is composed of oxygen, as well as calcium (a metal) and carbon (a non-metal).

Note also that words in a chemical name sometimes have prefixes attached to them, e.g. carbon *di*oxide. We shall discuss the meanings of such prefixes later.

4.3 Summary of Sections 3 and 4

Figure 4.3 contains flow diagrams for the most important chemical reactions that you met in Sections 3 and 4. The essential features can be summarized as follows:

1 Chemical reactions in sealed containers occur without any detectable change in mass.

2 Black copper oxide can be made either by heating copper in oxygen, or by dissolving copper in nitric acid, evaporating the solution, and strongly heating the solid that remains. In both cases, the copper emerges combined with oxygen, the oxygen having been supplied in the second case by nitric acid.

3 By either route, a particular mass of copper yields the same mass of black copper oxide, and that mass of copper is completely recovered by heating the oxide sample in hydrogen.

4 We say that copper oxide is composed of, or contains, copper and oxygen. Likewise, water is composed of hydrogen and oxygen.

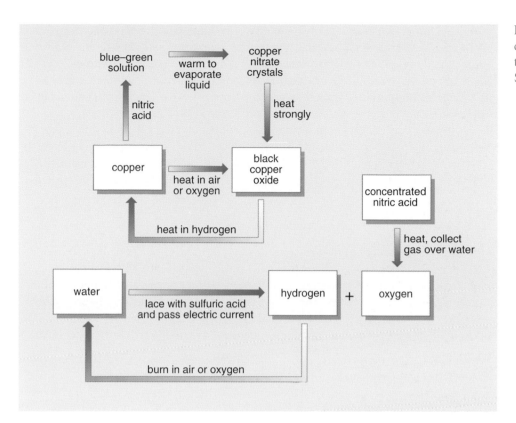

Figure 4.3 Reaction flow diagrams that summarize most of the reactions that you met in Sections 3 and 4.

5 Substances such as copper oxide and water, which can be broken down into constituents, are called chemical compounds. Substances such as copper, oxygen and hydrogen, which cannot be broken down, are called chemical elements.

6 There are millions of chemical compounds, but only about 100 chemical elements. Each chemical element is assigned a symbol, which consists of either one or two letters.

7 The chemical composition of a compound is a list of the percentages, by mass, of each chemical element that the compound contains. Any particular compound has its own characteristic composition.

8 When chemical compounds undergo chemical reactions, the masses of the chemical elements of which they are composed are unchanged: in chemical reactions, chemical elements are neither created nor destroyed.

9 The chemical names of binary compounds often consist of the names of the two constituent elements, with the second name modified to end in -ide. In names of binary compounds of metals and non-metals, the metal is written first. When the second name is modified to end in -ate, this tells us that the compound contains oxygen, in addition to the two named elements.

Sections 3 and 4 have introduced you to the concept of the chemical composition of a compound, and shown you how, in the cases of copper oxide and water, it can be determined. At the end of this section, Questions 4.1 and 4.2 and Activity 4.1 check your understanding of the concept and ask you to determine the chemical composition of the compounds lead oxide, silver chloride and hydrogen chloride.

Section 4 also put you in the way of thinking about chemical compounds in terms of the chemical elements that they contain. Question 4.3 will help you to get used to this idea.

Finally, Section 4 showed you how, when we have identified the chemical elements that some desirable product contains, we can immediately see that there are many combinations of starting materials from which it *cannot* be made. You can act on this idea in Question 4.4, and it shows that the concept of a chemical element is very powerful. However, we end on a critical note. Notice that the language that is a part of our distinction between elements and compounds is very strange. We have said that copper oxide is composed of, or contains, copper and oxygen, yet neither the redness of copper nor the colourless, gaseous nature of oxygen is in any way evident in the black powder that is copper oxide. So what important characteristics of copper and oxygen *are* present in copper oxide? To this question we shall turn in Section 5.

Question 4.1 When a porcelain boat containing 1.000 g of lead is heated in oxygen gas, as in Figure 3.3, the lead melts, and then reacts with the gas to form an orange powder. This is an oxide of lead. When the reaction is over, the contents of the boat now weigh 1.077 g. What is the chemical composition of the lead oxide? ◄

Question 4.2 When a porcelain boat containing 0.567 g of silver metal is heated in chlorine gas, the mass of the boat and its contents increases. When the increase in mass stops, the silver has been transformed into a white powder, which has a mass of 0.753 g. This is silver chloride; what is its chemical composition? ◄

Question 4.3 Use the names of the following substances to work out the chemical elements of which they are composed. In each case, use Table 4.2 to write down the names and symbols of the chemical elements. (a) Iron sulfide; (b) aluminium bromide; (c) zinc nitrate; (d) sodium bromate; (e) sodium hydrogen sulfate; (f) calcium carbide. ◄

Question 4.4 At the end of Section 2, we pointed out that an industry would be unwise to base its manufacture of the important chemical, nitric acid, on sodium nitrate from Chile. Use Table 4.1 to decide if nitric acid might be made from one of the following combinations: (a) calcium carbonate, sulfur and water; (b) air (a mixture, mainly of nitrogen and oxygen) and water; (c) common salt and sugar. Explain your conclusion. ◄

Activity 4.1 The chemical composition of hydrogen chloride

You saw hydrogen chloride being made, and then being dissolved in water, during Activity 2.1. Here, you can determine its chemical composition, and at the same time get some experience in experimental design. The activity is a little more demanding than Questions 4.1 and 4.2, and the result is more important. This is because it will be used later (Sections 7.8 and 8.3) when we try to compare the masses of different types of atom. ◄

The oxides of carbon

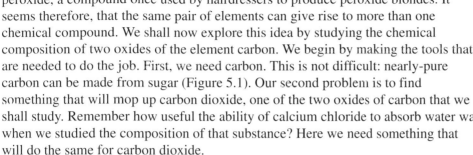

Water is a combination of the elements hydrogen and oxygen. But so is hydrogen peroxide, a compound once used by hairdressers to produce peroxide blondes. It seems therefore, that the same pair of elements can give rise to more than one chemical compound. We shall now explore this idea by studying the chemical composition of two oxides of the element carbon. We begin by making the tools that are needed to do the job. First, we need carbon. This is not difficult: nearly-pure carbon can be made from sugar (Figure 5.1). Our second problem is to find something that will mop up carbon dioxide, one of the two oxides of carbon that we shall study. Remember how useful the ability of calcium chloride to absorb water was when we studied the composition of that substance? Here we need something that will do the same for carbon dioxide.

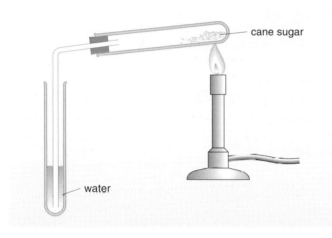

Figure 5.1 Making carbon: by dipping the end of the exit tube from the sealed test-tube in water, cane sugar can be heated strongly with only the most limited contact with air. Gases and water vapour are driven off, and black *sugar charcoal*, a form of carbon, is left in the test-tube.

We start with limestone (calcium carbonate), which contains calcium, carbon and oxygen. If it is strongly heated, to a temperature of over 1 000 °C, all of the carbon and some of the oxygen are lost as the gas, carbon dioxide, and there remains behind a lumpy white solid, which is composed of just calcium and oxygen. This is calcium oxide, commonly known as *quicklime*. Thus one possible word reaction for this change is:

limestone ⟶ quicklime + carbon dioxide   (5.1)

○ Rewrite this with proper chemical names.

○ calcium carbonate ⟶ calcium oxide + carbon dioxide   (5.2)

Now if the quicklime is cooled and dropped into a gas jar full of carbon dioxide, it will absorb the gas and regenerate calcium carbonate. In other words, reaction 5.2, which goes from left to right at 1 000 °C, goes from right to left at room temperature. It looks, therefore, as if quicklime is the carbon dioxide absorber that we need. But there is a problem. Quicklime also reacts with and absorbs water. To get round this, we add to the quicklime a strong solution of caustic soda or sodium hydroxide (the substance that you buy when you want to unblock drains) and then heat the mixture strongly until the water has evaporated. A white solid known as *soda lime* remains. This is also an excellent absorber of carbon dioxide, and it absorbs water vapour much less strongly than quicklime.

39

5.1 The composition of carbon dioxide

Carbon dioxide gas is formed when carbon burns in a plentiful supply of oxygen. Figure 5.2 shows how this reaction can be used to study the chemical composition of the gas. A weighed porcelain boat containing carbon is heated in a slow stream of dried oxygen gas. Some carbon burns in the oxygen, and forms carbon dioxide gas. The gas is carried downstream over heated copper oxide. The purpose of this will be fully explained later, but it ensures that all of the carbon that reacts is converted into carbon dioxide. The gas stream is then passed through a weighed tube of soda lime, which mops up the carbon dioxide. It is found that a 3.0 g decrease in the mass of the carbon boat is accompanied by an 11.0 g increase in the mass of the soda lime tube.

Figure 5.2 Determining the composition of carbon dioxide.

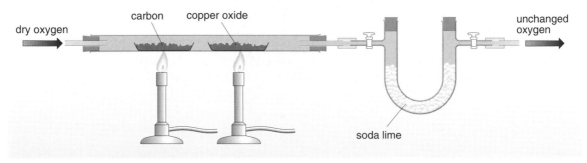

◉ When 3.0 g of carbon form carbon dioxide, how much oxygen does it combine with?

○ 3.0 g of carbon give 11.0 g of carbon dioxide. The mass of oxygen in the 11.0 g of carbon dioxide is the difference, $(11.0 - 3.0)$ g, which is 8.0 g.

5.2 A new oxide of carbon

If carbon is strongly heated in a slow current of carbon dioxide, a new gas, carbon monoxide, appears in the gas stream (Figure 5.3). Like carbon dioxide, it is a colourless gas that contains the elements carbon and oxygen and it is not very soluble in water, but there the resemblance ends. Carbon dioxide is a dense, non-combustible gas, and it is used in fire extinguishers. It is much denser than air, and can be poured down gutters like a liquid. Carbon monoxide has a density close to that of air, and burns with a beautiful blue flame. Most striking of all, so long as oxygen is mixed with it, we can safely breathe a gas containing quite high percentages of carbon dioxide; carbon monoxide, by contrast, is a deadly poison.

Figure 5.3 Carbon monoxide is obtained when carbon is strongly heated in a slow stream of carbon dioxide. The reaction is fast only above 1 000 °C, a temperature achieved using an electric furnace. The gas is freed of unchanged carbon dioxide in the soda lime trap. It can then be collected over water as in Figure 3.8, or burnt at the exit point as shown here. The flame has a beautiful blue colour.

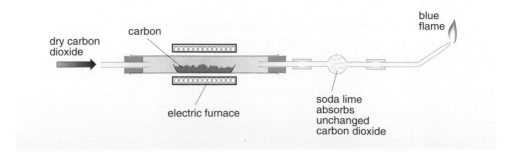

These marked differences in properties are associated with a big difference in chemical composition, and we shall now find out how big this difference is. We can use the fact that carbon monoxide is converted into carbon dioxide when it is passed over hot copper oxide:

carbon monoxide + copper oxide $\longrightarrow$ carbon dioxide + copper   (5.3)

Figure 5.4 shows how the experiment works.

Figure 5.4 Determining the composition of carbon monoxide: carbon monoxide is passed slowly over heated copper oxide. Some carbon monoxide is converted into carbon dioxide, which is then absorbed by the soda lime trap.

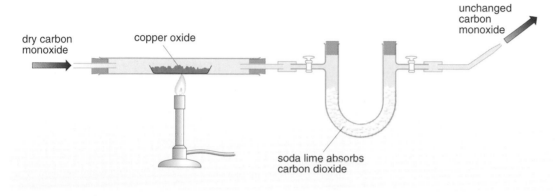

○ How do the masses of the boat (including its contents) and the soda lime trap change during the experiment?

○ The mass of the boat and its contents decreases as some of the copper oxide loses oxygen when carbon monoxide is converted into carbon dioxide; the soda lime trap increases in mass as this carbon dioxide is absorbed.

From this, we find that when the carbon dioxide absorbed by the soda lime has a mass of 11.0 g, then 4.0 g of oxygen are lost from the copper oxide in the boat.

Now Section 5.1 tells us that the 11.0 g of carbon dioxide contain 3.0 g of carbon and 8.0 g of oxygen. This carbon and oxygen must have come from the reactants in reaction 5.3: carbon monoxide and copper oxide. Of these reactants, only carbon monoxide contains carbon, so the 3.0 g of carbon must have come from this. Contributions to the 8.0 g of oxygen, however, come from both reactants. We know that 4.0 g have come from the copper oxide in the boat. Thus (8.0 − 4.0) g or 4.0 g have come from the reacting carbon monoxide.

○ So how much carbon and how much oxygen did the reacting carbon monoxide contain and what was its total mass?

○ It contained 3.0 g of carbon and 4.0 g of oxygen, so its total mass was 7.0 g.

To summarize, therefore, there exist two common oxides of carbon. In one of them, carbon monoxide (Box 5.1, *Carbon monoxide poisoning*), every 3.0 g of carbon are combined with 4.0 g of oxygen; in the other, carbon dioxide, every 3.0 g of carbon are combined with 8.0 g of oxygen. Of great importance is the fact that, in carbon dioxide, a particular mass of carbon is combined with *exactly twice* the mass of oxygen that this same mass of carbon is combined with in carbon monoxide. To make things simple, we derived this ratio of 2 from masses given to only one decimal place, but much more accurate masses give the same result. The best determinations give 1.999 95 ± 0.000 12! What can be the explanation of this simple ratio?

Box 5.1 *Carbon monoxide poisoning*

Most sudden deaths by poisoning are due to carbon monoxide. Whenever carbon compounds burn in an inadequate supply of air, there is danger of a build-up of this deadly gas. Faulty gas fires or water heaters are a particular risk; car exhaust fumes remain popular with suicides; those who die in fires are usually killed by carbon monoxide before their burns become fatal.

Oxygen gets carried around the body by combining with haemoglobin, the red pigment in blood. Carbon monoxide poisons by elbowing oxygen aside, and forming the compound carboxyhaemoglobin. Oxygen cannot then get into the bloodstream, and suffocation ensues. The carboxyhaemoglobin imparts a bright cherry-red colour to the victim's blood. Animals that do not rely on haemoglobin for oxygen transport are not at risk; lobsters, for example, remain cheerful at carbon monoxide levels that would kill human beings.

Exposure to carbon monoxide can be assessed by measuring the percentage of haemoglobin that has been converted into carboxyhaemoglobin by the gas. Figure 5.5 shows how after prolonged exposure, this depends on the amount of carbon monoxide in the atmosphere. It also gives typical symptoms at different exposures. Data banks suggest that most deaths occur at carboxyhaemoglobin levels of 50–70%.

Figure 5.5 A graph showing how the percentage of haemoglobin in blood that has been converted to carboxyhaemoglobin by carbon monoxide depends on the volume percentage of carbon monoxide, CO, in the air during a long exposure. Common symptoms at different levels are also given.

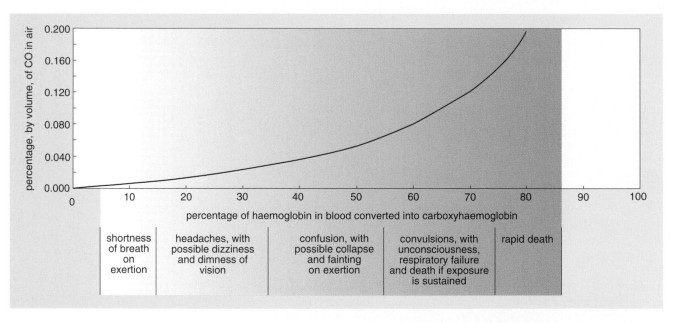

5.3   Explaining the simple ratio

Suppose that the element carbon, which we have used in the form of a black powder, is composed of tiny particles called atoms, which are all identical, most especially in their mass. Such atoms were *assumed* to exist, but without proof, in Block 2. Suppose likewise that the element oxygen, a gas, also contains identical atoms, but that their identical masses are different from that of a carbon atom. Now let us imagine that when carbon monoxide is formed from carbon and oxygen, every tiny carbon atom, which we represent ⚪, ends up linked to just one tiny oxygen atom, which we represent ⚪, in a tiny particle ⚪⚪ of carbon monoxide.

Now we have found that there are 3.0 g of carbon and 4.0 g of oxygen in 7.0 g of carbon monoxide. In 3.0 g of carbon, there will be some particular, but very large number of atoms. Let's call the number *one villion*. If each tiny carbon monoxide particle really is composed of one carbon atom and one oxygen atom, then the one villion atoms of carbon require one villion atoms of oxygen to form carbon monoxide. These one villion atoms of oxygen must therefore be present in the 4.0 g of oxygen that the 3.0 g of carbon combine with.

◯ So what would be the ratio of the mass of a carbon atom to the mass of an oxygen atom?

◯ 3 : 4; the mass of one carbon atom would be three grams divided by a villion, or three-villionths of a gram; the mass of one oxygen atom would be four grams divided by a villion, or four-villionths of a gram; the ratio is 3 : 4.

The argument is valid whatever number of atoms we assume to be present in 3.0 g of carbon. It is also pictured in Figure 5.6, where that number is assumed to be twelve, rather than a villion! It shows that this concept of atoms that we have introduced raises a most exciting possibility: if it is true, then the *relative* masses of the tiny, invisible atoms might be discernible in the large-scale combining masses that we weigh out in laboratories.

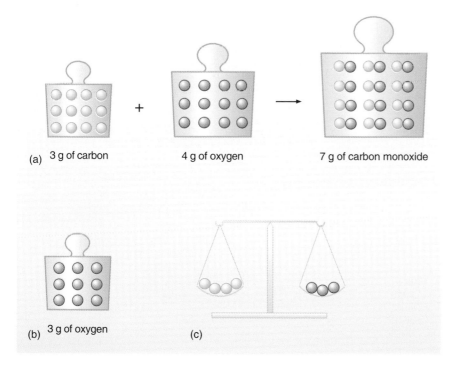

(a) 3 g of carbon   4 g of oxygen   7 g of carbon monoxide

(b) 3 g of oxygen   (c)

Figure 5.6 (a) 7.0 g of carbon monoxide (right) are composed of 3.0 g of carbon and 4.0 g of oxygen (left). If each tiny carbon monoxide particle is composed of one carbon atom and one oxygen atom, then, as shown, 3.0 g of carbon and 4.0 g of oxygen must each contain the same number of atoms. So, (b), 3.0 g of oxygen must contain three-quarters of the number of atoms in 3.0 g of carbon, and, (c), four carbon atoms must have the same mass as three oxygen atoms. Therefore each carbon atom must have a mass that is three-quarters of the mass of an oxygen atom.

But what evidence do we have that the idea makes sense? To answer this, let us turn to carbon dioxide. We have found that there are 3.0 g of carbon and 8.0 g of oxygen in 11.0 g of carbon dioxide.

○ If there are one villion carbon atoms in 3.0 g of carbon, and one villion oxygen atoms in 4.0 g of oxygen, how many oxygen atoms are there in the 8.0 g of oxygen contained in 11.0 g of carbon dioxide?

○ If there are one villion oxygen atoms in 4.0 g of oxygen, there will be two villion in 8.0 g. So the 11.0 g of carbon dioxide contain one villion carbon atoms in its 3.0 g of carbon, and two villion oxygen atoms in its 8.0 g of oxygen. In carbon dioxide, there are two oxygen atoms for every carbon atom.

So, if carbon monoxide really contains equal numbers of carbon and oxygen atoms, then it follows from the combining masses that, in carbon dioxide, the numbers of carbon and oxygen atoms are in the ratio 1 : 2. If we accept the simple atomic make-up of carbon monoxide (◯◯ particles), then the combining masses are evidence of a simple atomic make-up of carbon dioxide (◯◯◯ particles). It is this internal consistency that turns the chemical composition of the oxides of carbon into evidence for an atomic theory. The simple mass ratio that we set out to explain then marks the fact that in chemical compounds, the atoms of the chemical elements are combined in simple ratios.

An atomic theory

Not just carbon and oxygen, but many other pairs of chemical elements combine together to form more than one chemical compound. It then often turns out that, as in the case of the carbon oxides, the masses of one of the elements that combine with a fixed mass of the other, are in a simple numerical ratio. It follows that the **atomic theory** that we proposed in Section 5.3, the idea that substances are composed of atoms, is of general application. Now, therefore, we can state it in general terms. Three short propositions will cover and explain all the observations that we have made so far in this block.

1   The chemical elements are composed of very minute, indivisible particles of matter called atoms, which are preserved in all chemical changes.

2   All of the atoms of a particular element are identical, especially in mass. The different elements have atoms that differ in mass.

3   Chemical combination occurs by the union of the atoms of the elements in simple numerical ratios, e.g. one atom of A plus one atom of B; one atom of A plus two atoms of B; two atoms of A plus one atom of B; two atoms of A plus three atoms of B, etc.

The atomic theory was first put forward *in this form* by John Dalton (Figure 6.1).

Let us begin by seeing how the three propositions are consistent with our study of the carbon oxides. In that study, we assumed that the element carbon consists of carbon atoms, ⬤, and the element oxygen of oxygen atoms ⬤. When these elements combine to form carbon dioxide, each carbon links up to two oxygen atoms ⬤⬤⬤. The atoms are not destroyed in this process; they are preserved, and the changes that we see when the reaction happens are simply due to the linking up of the preserved atoms in a new way. This illustrates proposition 1.

Throughout our argument, we assumed that all carbon atoms had the same mass. Likewise, we assumed that all oxygen atoms had an identical mass, but this mass was different from that of a carbon atom. Indeed, our assumptions led to the conclusion that the mass of the carbon atom was close to three-quarters of that of an oxygen atom. This illustrates proposition 2.

We supposed that carbon monoxide was formed by the combination of carbon and oxygen atoms in the simple ratio $1 : 1$, and carbon dioxide by combination in the simple ratio $1 : 2$. This illustrates proposition 3.

Finally, you should know that all three of Dalton's propositions are, in some sense, wrong or misleading. Indeed, we shall later spend considerable time in setting two of them to rights. You may, perhaps, find it reprehensible that we should deliberately introduce a theory that is partly false. But that is what much of science is about: using theories until they are proved wrong, and then trying to improve them so that they can survive in the new situation (see Box 6.1, *Karl Popper: a scientists' philosopher?*).

Figure 6.1   John Dalton (1766–1844) was the son of a Cumberland weaver. A Quaker who spent much of his appallingly blameless life teaching, he remained a bachelor, remarking in his 20s that 'my head is too full of triangles, chemical processes and electrical experiments to think much of marriage'. His retiring character contrasts with the boldness of his scientific speculation to which the atomic theory is an enduring tribute. In the same spirit was his claim that he was colour blind to red because the aqueous medium in his eye was blue. He ordered that his eyes should be dissected after his death to test his theory. They were, and the tests proved the theory wrong. Think about this when you read Box 6.1.

Box 6.1   *Karl Popper: a scientists' philosopher?*

Most modern scientists show little interest in philosophical arguments about what science is. Karl Popper (Figure 6.2) came closest to breaking down this wall of indifference. By drawing on experience, including experimental results, scientists make up general statements about how the world works, rather in the way that we have put together a general atomic theory from experience of the composition of particular chemical compounds. This creation of general statements from particular observations is called *induction*. It is an essential part of science but, according to Popper, it is not what distinguishes science from other fields of study. Induction is an exercise of the imagination: it leads from what *is*, to what *might be*. Such creative moments, in which the imagination works on what is already known, are common to science, politics and the arts. Popper argues that what really distinguishes science from these other fields is the *form* of its general statements: in particular, they can be tested, and therefore falsified, by further observations and experiments. According to his *falsifiability criterion*, a statement can be scientific only if one can conceive of an observation or an experimental result that can logically prove it wrong.

Consider the following pair of statements:

1   The triumph of a World Communist revolution is inevitable.

2   Anyone who steps on to the surface of Mars will, within 10 minutes, be torn apart by bug-eyed monsters.

The first statement cannot be proved wrong, and so is not scientific: when teased about the lack of world revolutionary action, the true believer can always claim that Communism's hour, although coming, has not yet struck. By contrast, statement 2 is wholly scientific: we can imagine flying the Prime Minister to Mars in a spaceship, setting him down, and retiring to a safe distance to watch. If, after 15 minutes, he remains intact, we can fly home, and announce that statement 2 was false.

Notice that being scientific is not primarily about being right: most people would guess that the scientific statement 2 was untrue. This is crucial. When scientists propose a new hypothesis, Popper's concern is not so much that it should be right, but that it should be scientifically important, and testable by subsequent experiments. If the experiments falsify the hypothesis, then that's progress, because the search for a new and better theory can then begin. This view of science has opponents, but it is unquestionably exhilarating, and that partly explains its popularity with scientists. Experience combines with imagination to produce bold and exciting theories. But then, conscious that it may be wrong, science tries to destroy the fruits of its own imagination with experiments. Either error is exposed by falsification, or the theory survives — but survives only provisionally, because the next test may be just around the corner. So science never gives us final certainty or truth: it merely advances. And such advances begin when scientific practice exposes a weakness in scientific theory.

Figure 6.2   As a teenager, Karl Popper (1902–1994) was deeply impressed by Albert Einstein's willingness to specify experiments that might falsify his own theories. Popper's book, *The Logic of Scientific Discovery*, first appeared in 1934 in Vienna. He afterwards taught at universities in New Zealand and London. Once, at a Cambridge fireside, Popper argued about the status of philosophy with Ludwig Wittgenstein, who often urged philosophy students to take up something useful, like carpentry, instead. Things got heated, spawning the mischievous story that Popper and Wittgenstein had fought with pokers while Bertrand Russell acted as referee.

6.1   Elements, compounds and chemical symbols: a second look

In Section 4, we defined chemical elements as substances that could not be broken down into simpler constituents. The atomic theory now gives us a new insight into this difference between chemical elements and chemical compounds.

○   Why, according to the atomic theory, can chemical elements such as carbon, copper, oxygen and hydrogen not be broken down into simpler substances?

○   Because (proposition 1) they consist of identical *atoms*, which are indivisible.

By contrast, compounds such as copper oxide, water and carbon dioxide consist of different types of atom, intermingled and linked together in some way.

○   Why, according to the atomic theory, can a chemical compound, such as water, be broken down into simpler substances?

○   Because the combined hydrogen and oxygen atoms in water can be separated by a chemical reaction (Figure 6.3) into the element hydrogen, which contains just the hydrogen atoms, and the element oxygen, which contains just the oxygen atoms. The atomic theory allows this because, in the process, *the atoms themselves are not divided*.

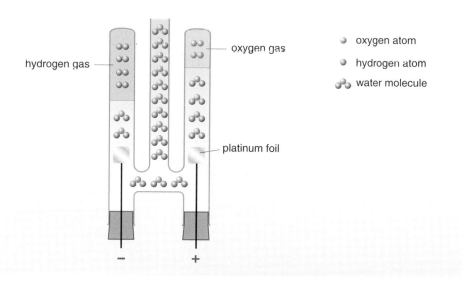

Figure 6.3   The atomic theory provides a new insight into the electrical decomposition of water shown in Figure 3.9. The water particles consist of hydrogen and oxygen atoms linked together. The experiment takes the water particles apart into hydrogen gas, an element that contains just the hydrogen atoms, and oxygen gas, an element that contains just the oxygen atoms. The figure anticipates facts that we shall establish later in the block: each water particle contains two hydrogen atoms and one oxygen atom; the particles in hydrogen gas and in oxygen gas consist of pairs of atoms.

This answers our earlier question (Section 4.3) about the strangeness of our language when we say that copper oxide contains copper and oxygen. What characteristics of red metallic copper and colourless oxygen gas could possibly be present in the black powder that is copper oxide? The answer is, the *atoms* of copper and the *atoms* of oxygen: they have merely been rearranged and intermingled in some way.

In Section 4.1, we introduced chemical symbols to represent the chemical elements. Thus the letter S represents the yellow solid that we know as sulfur. We also said that this was only one of two meanings that such a symbol can carry, and we can now introduce the second. According to the atomic theory, the atoms in yellow solid sulfur are all alike, but different from the identical atoms in, say, solid copper. So we also use the symbol S to represent the *type of atom* that is present in solid sulfur and all sulfur compounds.

A chemical composition like that of black copper oxide (79.9% Cu, 20.1% O) provides information about both types of meaning. First, it tells us that every 100 g of the compound can be taken apart into 79.9 g of red metallic copper and 20.1 g of colourless oxygen gas. Secondly, it tells us that black copper oxide is made up of copper atoms, which comprise 79.9% of its mass, and oxygen atoms, which comprise the remaining 20.1%.

6.2 A first look at chemical formulae

Proposition 3 of the atomic theory claims that chemical compounds are combinations of the atoms of the elements in simple numerical ratios. We can now represent such compositions by chemical formulae by writing, for example, carbon monoxide as CO, and carbon dioxide as CO_2. These formulae are pronounced 'see-oh' and 'see-oh-two'. In the **chemical formula** of a substance, the symbols for the chemical elements represent the *types of atom* that the substance contains. Thus the presence of C and O in the chemical formulae tells us that the oxides of carbon contain carbon and oxygen atoms. The formulae also contain numbers that appear as subscripts *after* the symbol for the type of atom to which they refer. Where no number appears after a symbol, that number is understood to be one. So CO means C_1O_1, and CO_2 means C_1O_2. The subscripts tell us the numerical ratios in which the atoms are combined. Thus CO_2 implies that, in carbon dioxide, the ratio of carbon to oxygen atoms is 1 : 2; every carbon atom is combined with two oxygen atoms. By contrast, the formula CO implies that, in carbon monoxide, that ratio is 1 : 1; every carbon atom is combined with just one oxygen atom.

Figure 6.4 Some important minerals: (a) calcite, which, like limestone, is one of the several forms of calcium carbonate ($CaCO_3$); (b) sphalerite (ZnS); (c) haematite (Fe_2O_3).

(a)

(b)

(c)

Figure 6.4 shows some minerals, along with their chemical formulae. Notice that if there is a metallic element in the formula, it is usual to write this first, just as in the naming of compounds (Section 4.2). Thus, calcium (Ca), zinc (Zn) and iron (Fe) are all metals and appear first; the non-metallic elements, such as carbon, sulfur and oxygen, come after. Oxygen in particular is nearly always placed last in any chemical formula of which it is a part.

○ What do the formulae for calcite and haematite tell you about the numerical combinations of atoms that they contain?

○ In calcite, every calcium atom is combined with one carbon atom and three oxygen atoms; the formula $CaCO_3$ means $Ca_1C_1O_3$, so the three types of atom occur in the ratio $1:1:3$. In haematite, every two iron atoms are combined with three oxygen atoms; the formula Fe_2O_3 shows that the iron and oxygen atoms occur in the ratio $2:3$.

In chemical formulae, therefore, a chemical symbol such as C, Fe or S represents a type of atom found in a particular chemical element, and the numbers tell us the ratios in which those types of atom are combined. This meaning differs from the one in which the symbols represent the elements themselves. When you meet chemical symbols, the context should reveal which of the two meanings is appropriate.

6.3   Chemical names and chemical formulae

The chemical names that were introduced in Section 4.2 revealed the constituent elements in a compound. But they can be adapted to reveal things about the chemical formula as well. You have seen that carbon forms two oxides: in CO, the ratio of oxygen atoms to carbon atoms is $1:1$; in CO_2, it is $2:1$. It is for this reason that the two oxides are called carbon *mon*oxide and carbon *di*oxide, respectively; the prefixes tell us the numbers in the ratios in which the atoms are combined. When the numbers in such ratios are three, four, five, six or seven, we use the prefixes tri-, tetra-, penta-, hexa- and hepta- respectively. Thus the metal chromium (Cr) combines with the gas fluorine (F) to form the compounds CrF_3, CrF_4, CrF_5 and CrF_6. These are called chromium trifluoride, chromium tetrafluoride, chromium pentafluoride and chromium hexafluoride, respectively. If both whole numbers in the ratio are greater than one, both elements get a prefix. Thus the oxide of chlorine, Cl_2O_7, is called dichlorine heptoxide.

○ Nitrogen forms compounds with the chemical formulae NCl_3 and N_2O_5. What are their names?

○ Nitrogen trichloride and dinitrogen pentoxide.

When two elements combine to form more than one compound, the prefixes will distinguish one compound from another. If just one compound is formed, there is no ambiguity, and it is common to omit the prefixes. Thus sodium and chlorine combine to form just NaCl; calcium and chlorine yield just $CaCl_2$. These compounds are usually called sodium chloride and calcium chloride, even though the formulae seem to require the names sodium monochloride and calcium dichloride.

Finally, some particular numerical combinations of the atoms of two different elements occur in so many chemical formulae, that they are called **chemical groups**, and given names of their own. An example that you have already met is the carbonate group, CO_3, which is found in calcium carbonate, $CaCO_3$. Other important examples from this block appear in Table 6.1, which also includes examples of the names of compounds that contain these groups.

Table 6.1 Some groups that occur in many chemical formulae.

Group	Group name	Name of sample compound	Formula of sample compound
CO_3	carbonate	disodium carbonate	Na_2CO_3
NH_4	ammonium	ammonium chloride	NH_4Cl
SO_4	sulfate	magnesium sulfate	$MgSO_4$
NO_3	nitrate	sodium nitrate	$NaNO_3$
PO_4	phosphate	trisilver phosphate	Ag_3PO_4
OH	hydroxide	sodium hydroxide	NaOH
ClO_4	perchlorate	silver perchlorate	$AgClO_4$

As with binary compounds, prefixes are commonly omitted when there is only one compound of the type in question. Thus there is only one compound formed from sodium and the carbonate group (Na_2CO_3). This is usually called sodium carbonate, rather than the more precise disodium carbonate used in Table 6.1. If in doubt, use the precise name and you won't go wrong.

6.4   A first look at chemical equations

When, as in Figure 5.3, carbon monoxide is made by heating carbon in carbon dioxide, the *word reaction* is:

$$\text{carbon + carbon dioxide} \longrightarrow \text{carbon monoxide} \tag{6.1}$$

Now we can replace words by chemical symbols:

$$C(s) + CO_2(g) \longrightarrow 2CO(g) \tag{6.2}$$

This is a **chemical equation**.[*]

Note first that after each chemical formula in the equation, there is a small letter in brackets. A bracketed 's' tells us that the substance is a solid, a bracketed 'l' that it is a liquid, and a bracketed 'g' that it is a gas. The chemical equation therefore tells us straight away that solid carbon reacts with gaseous carbon dioxide to give gaseous carbon monoxide. This gives us all the information that the word reaction does.

But there is more than this. Notice that the chemical formula of carbon monoxide in the equation is preceded by the number 2. No numbers appear before the formulae of carbon and carbon dioxide but, where this is the case, those numbers are understood to be 1. So the left-hand side of the equation tells us that for every carbon atom of the solid element carbon that reacts, one particle of carbon dioxide disappears as well. Thus two carbon atoms and two oxygen atoms have reacted in all. If there emerged from this change just one particle of carbon monoxide containing one carbon and one oxygen atom, then one carbon and one oxygen atom would have completely disappeared.

[*] In some textbooks, although not in S103, you may see chemical equations in which equals signs are used instead of arrows.

⬤ Why is this forbidden by the atomic theory?

◯ Proposition 1 states that atoms are preserved in all chemical changes; from a chemical point of view, they are indestructible.

It follows that *two* particles of carbon monoxide must be generated from the atom of carbon and the particle of carbon dioxide on the left-hand side of Equation 6.2. Only then will no atoms be created or destroyed, and the atomic theory be obeyed. This is why the chemical formula CO is preceded by a 2. We then have a **balanced chemical equation**: the numbers that precede each chemical formula in the equation are called **coefficients**, and have been adjusted so that each element that is involved in the chemical reaction appears with the same number of atoms on each side of the equation. All chemical equations should be balanced in this way. Only then does the equation reveal the correct ratios between the chemical formulae of the disappearing reactants and appearing products.

It is conventional to reduce the coefficients to the lowest possible whole-number values. For example, the equation

$$2C(s) + 2CO_2(g) \longrightarrow 4CO(g) \tag{6.3}$$

is correctly balanced: there are four carbon and four oxygen atoms on each side. But the preferred form is Equation 6.2 which is obtained from Equation 6.3 by dividing each coefficient by two. Figure 6.5 summarizes the essential qualities of a balanced chemical equation by using a different example.

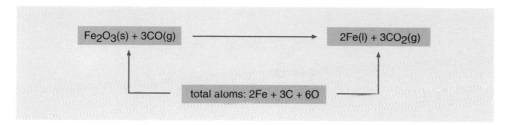

Figure 6.5 A balanced equation for a reaction that produces iron in a blast furnace: at about 1 400 °C, solid haematite reacts with carbon monoxide gas to give liquid iron and carbon dioxide gas. Each chemical formula is preceded, and therefore multiplied throughout, by a whole number. Thus $3CO_2$ contributes not just three carbon atoms to the right-hand side, but 3×2 or six oxygen atoms as well. The combination of chosen coefficients is such that, on both sides of the equation, there are equal numbers of the different types of atom. By convention, the smallest possible combination of whole numbers is chosen.

6.5 Methane and a burning question

In Section 5.3, chemical analysis told us that 7.0 g of carbon monoxide gas contain 3.0 g of carbon and 4.0 g of oxygen. When we discovered this, we used a chemical formula for the gas, CO, to deduce first that the mass of an oxygen atom is four-thirds that of a carbon atom, and secondly that the chemical formula of carbon dioxide is CO_2. But the formula CO was only a *guess*; if it is wrong, then these deductions will be wrong as well, and, in particular, the masses of the carbon and oxygen atoms will not stand in the ratio 3 : 4. To reinforce this point we now turn to the composition of another carbon compound.

Methane, once called marsh gas (Figure 6.6) is the chief constituent of natural gas. It is a **hydrocarbon**, one of many compounds containing just carbon and hydrogen. A typical sample of natural gas is 92% methane by volume, with 4% and 2% respectively of two other hydrocarbons, ethane and propane. A stream of methane

Figure 6.6 Methane was once called *marsh gas* because it appears when rotting vegetation at the bottom of a stagnant pond is stirred. The bubbles are easily collected and their flammability can then be demonstrated.

51

Figure 6.7 The blue flame of burning methane is seen when natural gas burns.

will burn smoothly with a familiar blue flame (Figure 6.7) but, as many accidents testify, if the gas first gets dispersed in air prior to ignition, an accidental spark can trigger off an explosive ball of fire. Methane can be released from coal seams, especially if there is a rock fall, and many coal miners have died in explosions of this kind (Box 6.2, *Methane, miners and moons*).

Box 6.2 Methane, miners and moons

'The wild fire proved my fatal destiny.' This epitaph appeared on Charles Braddow's gravestone after his death in Old Pinxton Colliery, Nottinghamshire in 1825. Wild fire was the name given by Midlands miners to the consuming flame of a methane explosion. Methane, known to miners as firedamp, is colourless, odourless and less dense than air. Before the 19th century, it was detected with a candle. This was placed on the floor of the mine, lit, and slowly raised. The sudden appearance of a blue colour in the spire of the flame marked the presence of methane. Once detected, the gas pocket could be cleared by the fireman. Dressed in rags that had been soaked in water, he crawled to the danger point, elevating before him a lit candle at the end of a long pole. When the explosion happened, he hugged the ground as the flame shot back over him along the roof above. A typical wage for such work was five shillings a day.

Large sources of methane, in the form of natural gas, exist on Earth, but the compound seems to be even more plentiful on some of the very cold outer planets and their satellites. On Pluto, the surface temperature is about −180 °C, and the planet is thought to be covered with solid methane 'ice' (Figure 6.8). On Titan, the largest of Saturn's moons, it is a little warmer, and it is possible that there are oceans of liquid methane. If so, their existence should be revealed when the Huyghens probe carried by the Cassini spacecraft makes its scheduled descent to the surface of Titan in 2004.

Figure 6.8 An artist's impression of the surface of Pluto. The feeble rays of the remote Sun are reflected from an icy covering of solid methane.

When methane burns in plenty of oxygen, the carbon that it contains combines with oxygen to form carbon dioxide, and the hydrogen that it contains combines with oxygen to form water vapour. The same products are formed when a slow stream of methane is passed over a heated sample of our old friend, copper oxide:

methane + copper oxide ⟶ carbon dioxide + water + copper   (6.4)

By weighing the carbon dioxide and water vapour that are formed in this reaction, we can determine the composition of methane. However, to make sure that the carbon in the methane is converted entirely into carbon dioxide, it is best to include oxygen in the methane stream.

Activity 6.1   An exercise in experimental design

In this activity you will first design an experiment to determine the composition of methane, and then calculate the composition from a typical set of experimental results. ◀

What Activity 6.1 showed you is that methane is 74.9% carbon and 25.1% hydrogen. So, to two significant figures:

> 75 g of carbon are combined with 25 g of hydrogen in 100 g of methane.

Dividing through by 25:

> 3.0 g of carbon are combined with 1.0 g of hydrogen in 4.0 g of methane.

Now when, in Section 5.3, we discussed the fact that there were 3.0 g of carbon and 4.0 g of oxygen in 7.0 g of carbon monoxide, we guessed the formula of carbon monoxide to be CO, and deduced that if this was so, then the masses of the carbon and oxygen atoms stood in the ratio 3 : 4. Suppose we now repeat this kind of exercise for methane, and assume that it consists of tiny particles with the simplest possible formula CH: each particle is a combination of one carbon and one hydrogen atom.

⬤ What will be the ratio of the mass of a carbon atom to the mass of a hydrogen atom?

◯ If 4.0 g of methane contain one villion particles of formula CH, then one villion atoms of carbon and one villion atoms of hydrogen will be present. The one villion atoms of carbon have mass 3.0 g and the one villion atoms of hydrogen have mass 1.0 g. So each carbon atom has mass of three-villionths of a gram, and each hydrogen atom has mass of one-villionth of a gram. The former is three times the latter.

So this argument, which starts with a chemical formula for methane, suggests that the masses of the hydrogen and carbon atoms stand in the ratio 1 : 3. Combining this result with the mass ratio of the carbon and oxygen atoms from Section 5.3, we conclude that the masses of the hydrogen, carbon and oxygen atoms stand in the ratio 1 : 3 : 4.

We have to tell you now that this is wrong. And it is wrong because the formula that we have guessed for methane is wrong. We have been trying to work out the relative masses of different atoms by guessing chemical formulae. But by guessing chemical formulae, we are building on sand. You cannot, it seems, get the relative atomic masses until you know chemical formulae, and you can't get the chemical formulae until you know the relative atomic masses. Only by extricating ourselves from the horns of this dilemma will we be able to find out how substances are built up from atoms. In Sections 7 and 8, you will see how this escape can be arranged.

Activity 6.2   Elements, compounds and the atomic theory

In this activity you will watch video demonstrations of some of the experiments that were used to advance the arguments of Sections 3–6. They also revise those arguments. ◄

6.6   Summary of Sections 5 and 6

Figure 6.9   A summary of the important chemical reactions in Sections 5 and 6. Chemical formulae are used only where they are correct, and have been an important part of the argument.

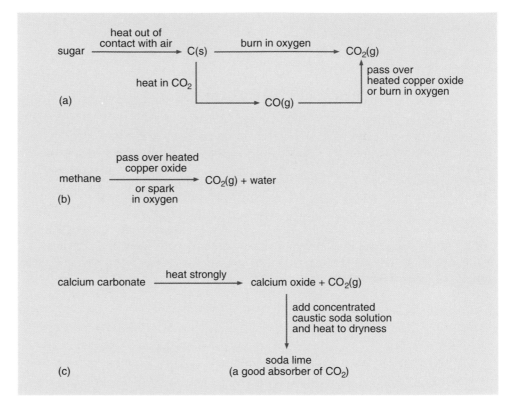

Figure 6.9 contains flow diagrams for the most important chemical reactions in Sections 5 and 6. The essential arguments are:

1   Carbon combines with oxygen to form two colourless, odourless gaseous oxides. The first, carbon monoxide, is very toxic, burns in oxygen with a blue flame and has a density similar to that of air. The second, carbon dioxide, extinguishes fires and is much denser than air.

2   If you determine the mass of oxygen that is combined with a particular mass of carbon in both carbon monoxide and carbon dioxide, you find that the first mass of oxygen is half the second. Simple ratios like this are found in other cases in which two particular elements combine to form more than one compound.

3   The ratios can be explained by a simple atomic theory in which each chemical element consists of identical, indestructible atoms with a characteristic mass. Chemical compounds are formed by combination of the atoms of the elements in simple numerical ratios. Then, for example, if carbon monoxide has the formula CO, that of carbon dioxide must be CO_2.

4   In these chemical formulae, the individual symbols stand for one atom of an element, and the formulae tell us the ratios in which the atoms of different elements are combined within chemical compounds.

5   Chemical equations are put together by replacing names in word reactions by chemical formulae. As atoms are preserved in all chemical reactions, such equations must be balanced: the same number of atoms of each element must appear on both sides of the equation.

6   Methane, the main ingredient of natural gas, is a hydrocarbon. It is colourless, odourless and flammable, forming carbon dioxide and water when it burns in oxygen or reacts with hot copper oxide.

7   We have a dilemma: until we know chemical formulae, we cannot use chemical compositions to calculate relative atomic masses; and until we know relative atomic masses we cannot use chemical compositions to calculate chemical formulae.

Sections 5 and 6 have introduced the atomic theory, and points 3, 4, 5 and 7 summarize its essentials. In Question 6.1, you can check your understanding of the discussion of the formulae of the oxides of carbon in the text by carrying out a similar exercise on the oxides of copper. This will demonstrate the dilemma of point 7: the relative atomic masses of copper and oxygen are obtained only after guessing the chemical formula of black copper oxide. Questions 6.2 and 6.3 will increase your familiarity with chemical formulae, and in Question 6.4 you can try your hand at balancing a chemical equation, although systematic practice in this will come later (Section 9).

Notice that the concept of a chemical element has taken on a new meaning in Sections 5 and 6. From being a substance that cannot be broken down into components, it has become something composed of just one type of atom. The old meaning remains valid, but it has been incorporated into the new one, which explains more and shows greater promise. This adaptability in the face of new discoveries is characteristic of the best scientific concepts, and, as you will see, for the concept of a chemical element it has not yet run its course. Adaptation of this sort emphasizes the *provisional* nature of scientific theory, a point we made in the philosophical digression of Box 6.1.

In Activities 6.4 and 6.5 you will practise two new skills. In Activity 6.5, you will use what you have learnt to criticize someone else's chemistry, and then write up your critique as a short paragraph. In Activity 6.4 you are asked to draw on both graphical and written information and then give an opinion about a death that has occurred in suspicious circumstances.

Finally, you may have found it hard to keep a complete grip on the argument that was developed in Sections 3–6. If so, Activity 6.3 gives you a chance to revise and review both it, and the use of the scientific method.

Question 6.1   In Sections 3.3 and 3.4, we found that when copper formed black copper oxide, every 1.000 g of copper combined with 0.252 g of oxygen, and that the chemical composition of the oxide is therefore 79.9% copper and 20.1% oxygen.

(a) Suppose that in black copper oxide there is one copper atom for every oxygen atom. Write a chemical formula for the compound.

(b) If this guessed formula is correct, what is the ratio of the mass of a copper atom to the mass of an oxygen atom?

(c) It is also possible to make another oxide of copper, which is red and has the composition 88.8% copper and 11.2% oxygen. Calculate the mass of copper that is combined with 0.252 g of oxygen in red copper oxide. Assuming that the formula that we guessed for black copper oxide is correct, what is the chemical formula of red copper oxide? ◀

Question 6.2   Sulfuric acid has the chemical formula H_2SO_4. What is the ratio between the numbers of hydrogen, sulfur and oxygen atoms in this compound? How many oxygen atoms are there for every hydrogen atom? ◀

Question 6.3   The metals magnesium and aluminium both form white solid compounds when they are heated in chlorine gas. In the magnesium compound there are two chlorine atoms for every magnesium atom; in the aluminium compound, there are three chlorine atoms for every aluminium atom. Name, and write a chemical formula for, each compound.

Aluminium also burns in oxygen at high temperatures, forming a white solid oxide in which there are three oxygen atoms for every two aluminium atoms. Name, and write a chemical formula for, this oxide. ◀

Question 6.4   Iron forms two solid chlorides: iron dichloride, $FeCl_2$, which is colourless, and iron trichloride, $FeCl_3$, which is reddish brown. When iron trichloride is heated in a sealed tube with metallic iron, iron dichloride is formed:

$$Fe(s) + FeCl_3(s) \longrightarrow FeCl_2(s)$$

Explain why this equation is not balanced. Now try to balance it by putting the appropriate coefficients before the chemical formulae in the equation. Start by inserting coefficients before $FeCl_3$ and $FeCl_2$ to get the same number of chlorine atoms on each side of the equation. ◀

Activity 2.2   A glossary of chemicals (continued)
This is an appropriate point at which to include chemicals from Sections 3–6 in your glossary. ◀

Activity 6.3   Using the scientific method: reviewing the argument in Sections 3–6
In this activity you will combine practice in the scientific method with a review of what you have learnt. ◀

Activity 6.4   Using the scientific method: combining sources of evidence to formulate an opinion
In this activity you are asked to play the rôle of a forensic scientist by deciding whether there is anything suspicious about a death from carbon monoxide poisoning. ◀

Activity 6.5   Using your knowledge to write critically about somebody else's chemistry
Edgar Wallace was the most successful thriller writer of the 1920s. In this activity you are asked to criticize his understanding of the chemistry of the oxides of carbon. ◀

Getting to know gases

At the end of Section 6, we met a dilemma: to find relative atomic masses, we need chemical formulae, but to get chemical formulae, we need relative atomic masses. This problem will be solved in Sections 7 and 8 by studying the properties of gases. The story is quite a complex one, but Activity 7.1 should help you to follow the main points.

Activity 7.1   Keeping hold of the argument in Sections 7 and 8

This activity provides you with a conceptual flow chart for Sections 7 and 8, together with a reviewing procedure that you can follow as you study. ◀

7.1   Pressure

Throughout Section 7, we shall be especially concerned with pressure in *gases*, but it is convenient to start with pressure in liquids. You were introduced to the concept of pressure in Box 6.1 of Block 2. It was defined as the force acting on a surface divided by the area of that surface. Consider swimmers who dive deeply into water. They first experience the extra pressure through their ears, and this is often attributed to the 'weight of water' bearing down on them. The 'weight of water' is a force that acts on the surface area of the eardrum.

This phrase catches the important dependence of pressure on depth. What it misses is the fact that the pressure at any point in a liquid is not just exerted in a downward sense: *it is transmitted equally in all directions*. No matter how the swimmer's head is inclined, the same discomfort is caused to the eardrums. This, together with the dependence of pressure on depth, brings us to an important conclusion: if there is some uninterrupted pathway, however crooked, between two points at the same horizontal level in, or at the surface of, a liquid, the pressure at those two points will be the same (Figure 7.1).

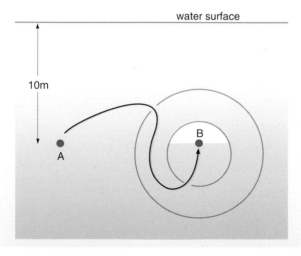

Figure 7.1   Two concentric hollow spheres immersed in water are both holed, but the inner sphere contains trapped air. There is no 'weight of water' bearing directly down on a swimmer at B, but there is an uninterrupted pathway through water from points such as A which are at the same level outside the spheres. So the pressure on the swimmer at B is the same as at A which has 10 m of water above it.

The plight of the swimmer in Figure 7.1 resembles that of the crew of a breached submarine. Box 7.1, *The perils of submarine warfare*, is a vivid reminder of the pressure that the sea exerts at quite modest depths. But as you were told in Block 2 Section 6.2, we ourselves are never free of pressure from the ocean of air in which we live. Let us look at this in more detail.

Box 7.1 The perils of submarine warfare

On 22 April 1918, the German submarine UB-55 dived and struck a British mine in the Straits of Dover. Kapitan-Leutnant Wenniger takes up the tale:

Water poured in astern and the boat sank to the bottom at 40 metres depth. Increasing pressure brought pain in the ears and breathing became difficult. Two men shot themselves, and I myself thought of taking morphine, but Dollman persuaded me to bear it a little longer. Eventually, I found myself able to open the conning tower hatch. For a moment, I stood in front of a dark, black greenish wall. Then the water broke all over me and I began to rise. I had a sense of increasing in size, and was astonished to find that I had no desire to inhale, but forcibly exhaled so that I was constantly blowing air out of my cheeks. I therefore moved my hands to slow my ascent.

Before leaving the boat, I had not inflated my lifebelt, and only closed the valve to keep the water out. When I broke surface, I found it fully inflated. About 20 of the crew got out of a torpedo hatch and came up very quickly, some screamed when they surfaced, and sank again. These poor men had held their breath and made a rapid ascent. Eight of us were eventually rescued by a British patrol.

7.2   Atmospheric pressure

Few substances have made a greater contribution to the growth of scientific understanding than mercury (Figure 7.2). Two very simple, but visionary experiments on pressure testify to this. The first was performed at Florence in 1644 under the direction of Evangelista Torricelli. A glass tube about one metre long was sealed at one end. Torricelli's assistant filled the tube to the brim with mercury, and stoppered it with his thumb. He then inverted the tube, placed the stoppered end beneath the surface of a trough containing more mercury and removed his thumb. The mercury inside the tube began to fall back into the trough; but then it stopped. Its surface was then about 75 cm above the surface of the mercury in the trough beneath (Figure 7.3).

Figure 7.2   The metal mercury is a liquid at room temperature (Figure 4.1c). Its density is 13.6 times that of water, and as a result, it supports the man like a cushion. This photograph was taken in the early 1970s at the famous Almaden mercury mine in Spain. Today, EU safety regulations would prohibit such delights.

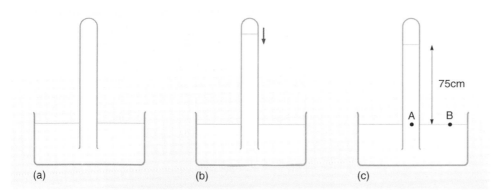

Figure 7.3 Torricelli's experiment: the mercury in the completely filled tube in (a) drops back, (b), until its surface is about 75 cm above the surface of the mercury in the trough, (c).

Torricelli had an explanation for all this. Let's apply what you learnt in Section 7.1.

○ How do the pressures at points A and B in Figure 7.3c compare?

○ They must be the same; they are at the same horizontal level, and there are uninterrupted pathways from one to the other through the mercury.

Now, pressing down on any small horizontal area around point A is a column of mercury 75 cm high. But there appears to be nothing pressing down on a similar area around point B. So how can the pressures at A and B be the same? Torricelli's answer was that 'we live submerged in a vast ocean of air, and the air is heavy'. There is a column of *air* pressing down on the area around B. When the mercury begins to fall in Figure 7.3b, it leaves a vacuum behind it: the space above the mercury inside the tube contains no air, and exerts no significant pressure. So the fall continues until the pressure on A of the mercury column alone, just matches the pressure of the Earth's atmosphere on B. The height of the mercury inside the tube (75 cm) is a direct measure of the atmospheric pressure outside the tube at the surface of the mercury in the trough.

This idea was later taken up by a young French cleric, Blaise Pascal, in Rouen. The best science is the kind that can predict the results of untried experiments. Pascal's brother-in-law, Florin Périer, lived in Clermont, and ten miles west is the Puy-de-Dôme, whose summit stands 1 200 m above the city (Figure 7.4). Pascal wrote, asking Périer to try the Torricelli experiment in Clermont, and then to immediately climb the Puy-de-Dôme and repeat it.

○ If Torricelli was right, should the height of the mercury inside the tube be greater or less at the summit of the Puy-de-Dôme?

○ Pascal thought it should be less; climbing a mountain should diminish the height of the column of air above us. The atmospheric pressure should fall.

On 19 September 1648, Périer set up two versions of Figure 7.3c in the garden of the Pères Minimes monastery in Clermont. In both, the height of the mercury was 71 cm. Asking a monk to keep an eye on one of them, he carried the other to the top of the Puy-de-Dôme. There, he found that the height of the mercury had fallen to 63 cm. When he returned a few hours later, he found that in the Pères Minimes, 71 cm was still the order of the day. Pascal's prediction had been proved right: what you see here is science at its best.

Two final points: first the Puy-de-Dôme experiment shows that atmospheric pressure decreases by only about 11% over an altitude of 1 200 m. So over distances that are

Figure 7.4 The Puy-de-Dôme near Clermont in France, the site of Pascal's famous experiment.

comparable with the sizes of equipment used in experiments with gases (sealed bulbs or balloons with a diameter of about 0.2 m) any such changes will be negligible. This means that we can regard the pressure of the gas in a sealed container as being everywhere the same. Secondly, we have begun using the height of a mercury column as a measure of pressure. It seems, for example, that a typical atmospheric pressure is the same as that exerted by a 75 cm column of mercury. The unit of atmospheric pressure used in Block 2 was the bar. Under the conditions in which measurements are made in this block, it turns out that 75 cm of mercury is equivalent to 1.00 bar, or the 1 000 millibars quoted in a typical weather forecast.

7.3   Pressure and gas volume: Boyle's law

In the last section, we spoke of the pressure of a gas, but how can we measure this pressure? Suppose that you stop the exit hole of a bicycle pump with your finger, and push in the piston with some force (Figure 7.5a). This increased force increases the pressure acting on the trapped air, and its volume decreases. Eventually the piston stops moving (Figure 7.5b) and, in this static situation, the pressure that you are applying to the gas through the piston is exactly balanced by the pressure that the gas exerts on the piston and on the other surfaces with which it is in contact: the two are equal. In other words, in these static situations, the pressure acting *on* the gas and the pressure *of* the gas are the same, so we can determine the latter by measuring the former. In this section, we shall use such measurements to work out the precise relationship between the pressure and the volume of a gas.

Figure 7.5   Gases are rather elastic. If the exit hole of a bicycle pump is stopped (a), the volume of the contained air decreases substantially as you push in the piston with increasing force, until a balance is reached (b).

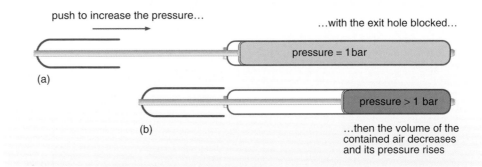

The equipment is shown in Figure 7.6. It consists of a U-shaped glass tube, the two arms being of very different lengths. The short arm is sealed; the long arm is left open, and has a funnel attached for easy filling. A little mercury is poured in. By jiggling the tube around to allow some of the air trapped in the short arm to escape past the blocking mercury, the situation of Figure 7.6a is achieved. Here, a reasonably large volume of air has been trapped in the short arm, and the levels of mercury in the long and short arms are the same. We now measure atmospheric pressure with a Torricelli barometer of the type shown in Figure 7.3c and find it is 75 cm of mercury.

⬤ What is the pressure of the trapped air in Figure 7.6a?

⚪ This too is equivalent to 75 cm of mercury. The situation is static so the pressure of the trapped air is equal to the pressure exerted on it at A by the mercury. This is equal to the pressure on B, which is at the same level in the mercury as A. The pressure on B is the atmospheric pressure of 75 cm.

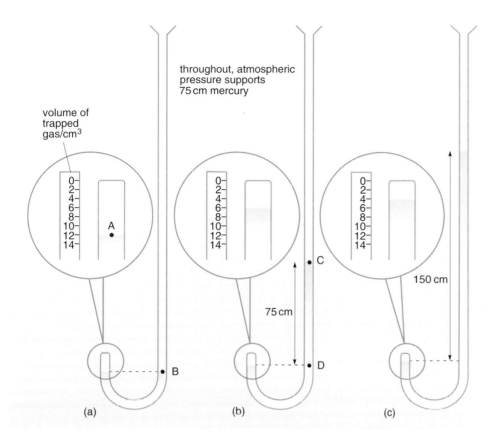

volume of trapped gas/cm³

throughout, atmospheric pressure supports 75 cm mercury

Figure 7.6 One arm of a U-tube is open; the other is sealed and contains air (encircled) which is trapped by mercury. Throughout, the atmospheric pressure is 75 cm of mercury. In (a), the mercury level in both arms is the same. In (b) and (c), mercury has been poured into the open arm until the excess height is 75 cm in (b), and 150 cm in (c). The volume of air is then one-half and one-third, respectively, of what it was in (a).

Set against the trapped air is a scale, which tells us its volume; in Figure 7.6a, this is 12 cm³. Now mercury is carefully poured in to the long arm where its level gradually rises. Pouring stops when the level in the long arm is exactly 75 cm above the level in the short arm (Figure 7.6b). The temperature remains constant throughout.

○ In Figure 7.6b, what are the pressures at C and D?

○ Above C is just the atmosphere, so the pressure at C is just the atmospheric pressure of 75 cm of mercury. Below C, there is a 75 cm column of mercury before we get to D. So the pressure at D is the pressure at C plus 75 cm of mercury. This is 150 cm of mercury in all.

○ So what is the pressure of the trapped air in Figure 7.6b, and how has its volume altered?

○ The pressure is 150 cm of mercury: as before, it is equal to the pressure at D. The scale against the trapped air shows that its volume has decreased to 6 cm³.

Thus in moving from Figure 7.6a to 7.6b, the pressure of the trapped air has been doubled, and in response, its volume has halved. In Figure 7.6c, more mercury has been poured in so that the level in the long arm rises until it is 150 cm above that in the short arm. Now the pressure of the trapped gas is 225 cm of mercury: three times what it was in Figure 7.6a. At the same time, the gas volume has fallen to 4 cm³: one-third of what it was in Figure 7.6a.

○ What do you get when you multiply the pressure of the gas by its volume in Figures 7.6a–c?

○ For Figure 7.6a, the pressure multiplied by the volume is (75 cm of mercury) × 12 cm³ = 900 (cm of mercury)(cm³). Similarly in (b) and (c), the pressure multiplied by the volume has exactly the same value.

○ Now predict what the gas volume would become if the pressure were raised to 300 cm of mercury.

○ 3 cm³, because (300 cm of mercury) × 3 cm³ = 900 (cm of mercury)(cm³).

What we have just done is to use the results of the experiments in Figure 7.6 to elicit **Boyle's law**:

> At constant temperature, the pressure of a fixed mass of gas multiplied by its volume is a constant.

We can express this as a word equation:

$$\text{pressure} \times \text{volume} = \text{constant} \tag{7.1}$$

In mathematical symbols, if the pressure is P and the volume is V:

$$PV = \text{constant} \tag{7.2}$$

If you were successful in predicting the volume of 3 cm³ at a pressure of 300 cm³ mercury, then you have used Equation 7.2 to work out the volume of a gas at one pressure from the volume that it has at another. We shall use the equation for this purpose when measuring gas densities in Section 7.6.

7.4 Temperature and gas volume: Charles' law

We have now established how the volume of a gas varies with pressure when its temperature is fixed. How does its volume vary with the temperature when the pressure is fixed? Figure 7.7 shows how to find out. The gas sample is trapped in a sealed tube by a drop of mercury and is subject throughout to atmospheric pressure. Alongside is a scale off which the volume can be read. Suppose the heat-bath in which the tube is immersed is first set at a temperature of 0 °C, and that the volume of the gas is then 1.000 cm³, as in Figure 7.7. Now the temperature of the heat bath is gradually raised to 100 °C, the boiling temperature of water. The mercury drop moves to the right as the gas expands, and the new volume at 100 °C is read off the scale. Now the bath temperature is raised to 200 °C and a further volume reading is taken. Table 7.1 shows the results when the experiment is performed with six different gases; in each case, it starts with 1.000 cm³ of gas at 0 °C. The results are very remarkable.

○ Why are they remarkable?

○ Because changing the gas makes little or no difference to the results. Whether we start with life-sustaining oxygen or deadly carbon monoxide, with explosive hydrogen or inert nitrogen, the initial 1.000 cm³ of gas expands by about 0.367 cm³ between 0 °C and 100 °C. It then expands by about a further 0.367 cm³ between 100 °C and 200 °C.

On cooling, these changes are reversed.

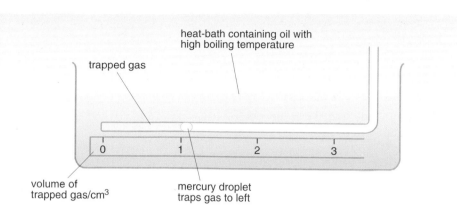

heat-bath containing oil with high boiling temperature

trapped gas

volume of trapped gas/cm³

mercury droplet traps gas to left

Table 7.1 The change in volume of 1 cm³ of six different gases when the temperature changes from 0 °C to 100 °C, and then to 200 °C, at a constant atmospheric pressure.

Gas	Volume (0 °C) /cm³	Volume (100 °C) /cm³	Volume (200 °C) /cm³
air	1.000	1.367	1.734
carbon dioxide	1.000	1.371	1.742
carbon monoxide	1.000	1.367	1.733
hydrogen	1.000	1.366	1.732
nitrogen	1.000	1.367	1.735
oxygen	1.000	1.367	1.734

○ From the data in Table 7.1, is the volume *proportional to* the temperature in °C?

○ No, it is not. If it were, a doubling of the temperature (from 100 °C to 200 °C) would lead to a doubling of the volume (from 1.37 cm³ to 2.74 cm³). As you can see, the volume increase is much less than this.

The volumes do, however, become proportional to the temperature if we use the absolute temperature scale, which was introduced in Block 5. The zero for this scale is called the absolute zero, and has a temperature of –273 °C (to the nearest degree). To obtain temperatures on the absolute scale, one simply adds 273 to the number of degrees Celsius; the unit of the new scale is called the kelvin (K).

○ To what absolute temperatures do 0 °C, 100 °C and 200 °C correspond?

○ 273 K, 373 K and 473 K, respectively.

In Figure 7.8, the volumes in Table 7.1 have been plotted against these absolute temperatures. As you can see, the result is a straight line that goes through the origin. This is a sign that the volumes are proportional to the absolute temperatures:

$$V \propto T$$

But Box 3.1 of Block 5 showed that a proportionality like this can be written:

$$V = \text{constant} \times T \tag{7.3}$$

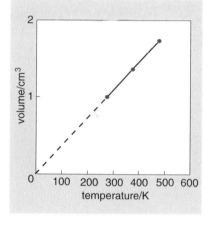

Figure 7.8 When the volumes of Table 7.1 are plotted against *absolute* temperature, the result is a straight line which, if extended downwards, goes through the origin. This is a sign that the volumes are *proportional to* the absolute temperatures. Note that the downward extension suggests that if the contraction observed between 200 °C and 0 °C continues, the gas volume will become zero at 0 K (–273 °C). We comment on this result in Section 7.5.

So dividing both sides by T:

$$\frac{V}{T} = \text{constant} \tag{7.4}$$

This is known as **Charles' law**.

> At constant pressure, the volume of a fixed mass of gas divided by the absolute temperature is a constant.

Now let's check that Charles' law really works for the data in Table 7.1. At 200 °C, the volume of the hydrogen sample is 1.732 cm³. As 200 °C is 473 K, for this sample

$$\frac{V}{T} = \frac{1.732 \, \text{cm}^3}{473 \, \text{K}} \tag{7.5}$$

Now according to Charles' law, this value of $\frac{V}{T}$ is constant if the pressure is not changed.

○ What would be the volume of the sample at 0 °C?

○ As 0 °C is 273 K, the volume V at this temperature is given by

$$\frac{V}{273 \, \text{K}} = \frac{1.732 \, \text{cm}^3}{473 \, \text{K}} \tag{7.6}$$

so

$$V = \frac{1.732 \, \text{cm}^3 \times 273 \, \text{K}}{473 \, \text{K}}$$

$$= 1.00 \, \text{cm}^3 \tag{7.7}$$

This agrees with the value in Table 7.1. Indeed, it is a consequence of Charles' law that at constant pressure, the volume of a gas at 0 °C is $\frac{273}{473}$ or 57.7% of its volume at 200 °C. We shall use this result when measuring gas densities in Section 7.8.

Activity 7.2   Combining Boyle's and Charles' laws

So far you have used Boyle's law to work out how the volume of a sample of gas changes with pressure, and Charles' law to work out how it changes with temperature. Now suppose that both the pressure and the temperature are changed; how does one work out the new volume then? This activity checks that you can do this. ◀

7.5   Revisiting the particle model of a gas

Let us now try to understand the results of Sections 7.3 and 7.4 by revisiting the model that was introduced in Block 2, Section 6.1. There, we suggested that a gas was a collection of identical, tiny particles. Now, the atomic theory allows us to expand on what we mean by identical. In carbon monoxide, for example, each particle is identical in that it is composed of one carbon and one oxygen atom. These tiny particles of which gases are composed are called **molecules**.

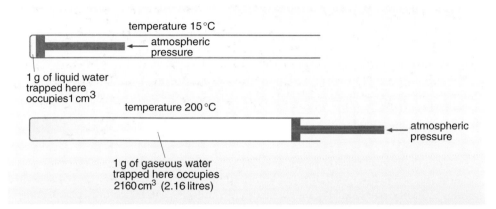

Figure 7.9 One gram of liquid water, which occupies a volume of only 1 cm^3 at 15 °C, expands to approximately 2 160 cm^3 or 2.16 litres when it becomes a gas at 200 °C under atmospheric pressure. Note that the two volumes are not to the same scale in this diagram.

At normal pressures, the molecules in a gas must be much farther apart than in solids or liquids. Observations like the one in Figure 7.9 tell us this. When liquids boil and change into gases, the molecules suddenly find themselves in a space many times larger than the one that they occupied in the liquid state. They must therefore be much farther apart.

In Block 2, these molecules were pictured as tiny, fast-moving spheres. The pressure that gases can exert is then explained by the unceasing collisions of the tiny molecules against the walls of their container. This allows us to explain qualitatively why an increase in external pressure decreases the volume of a gas (Figure 7.10). Boyle's law (Section 7.3) connects that pressure increase and volume decrease in a quantitative way.

Next we turn to the effect of an increase in temperature on the volume of a gas at fixed pressure. In Block 2, Section 6.1, it was assumed that as a gas gets hotter, the average speed of its molecules increases. Figure 7.11 uses this idea to explain qualitatively how an increase in temperature empowers the gas molecules to drive back the containing mercury and increase the gas volume. Charles' law (Section 7.4) connects these two increases in a quantitative way.

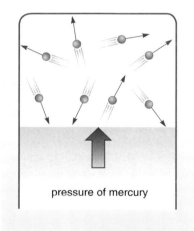

Figure 7.10 The trapped gas in Figure 7.6; the vertical arrow in the mercury indicates *pressure* not movement. When the mercury level is stationary, our model suggests that the mercury is kept at bay by the collisions of the gas molecules on its surface. They also drum on the walls of the containing glass above the mercury. If the upward pressure from the mercury is increased, the drumming is no longer sufficient to hold back the mercury, and the mercury level rises as the gas molecules are forced to retreat. As they do so, the volume that they occupy decreases. This is why an increase in external pressure decreases the volume of a gas.

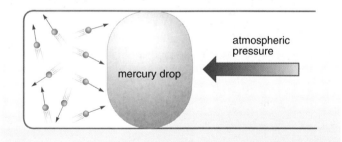

Figure 7.11 The trapped gas of Figure 7.7. The horizontal arrow indicates the influence of (atmospheric) pressure. Again, the drumming of the moving molecules on the surface of the mercury drop holds the drop at bay. An increase in temperature increases the average speed of the gas molecules. They therefore drum more violently on the mercury surface, and they also hit the surface more frequently. The mercury drop therefore retreats. This is why an increase in temperature increases the volume of the gas.

Lastly we return to the strange conclusion suggested by Charles' law in the caption to Figure 7.8: if a gas kept at constant pressure continues in the steady contraction that we observed between 200 °C (473 K) and 0 °C (273 K), its volume will become zero at –273 °C (0 K)

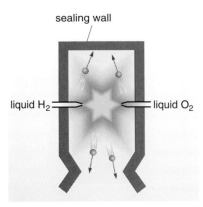

Figure 7.12 The engine of a rocket: liquid hydrogen and liquid oxygen are injected into a hollow cylinder with a sealing wall at the top. The two liquids enflame to a high temperature on contact, and very fast-moving water molecules are produced. Downward-moving molecules escape, but upward moving ones drum on the sealing wall and lift the rocket off.

○ Can you suggest one reason why the steady contraction will *not* continue?

○ If they are cooled sufficiently, *all* gases are converted into solids or liquids.

These changes to a solid or liquid always occur before the absolute zero is reached. For example, methane becomes liquid at −162 °C, oxygen at −183 °C, carbon monoxide at −192 °C, nitrogen at −196 °C and hydrogen at −253 °C. In Block 2, Section 6.1, this was explained by the presence of significant *attractive* forces between the gas molecules at short ranges. Although these intermolecular forces are significant, when a collision brings two gas molecules together, the attractive force is not strong enough to bind them as a pair and prevent them escaping each other's clutches. But if the relative motion of the gas molecules is made less vigorous by cooling, the intermolecular forces eventually become dominant, colliding molecules begin to hang together, and a solid or liquid is formed. When liquefied in this way, hydrogen and oxygen occupy a much smaller volume than they do as gases, and can then be used to drive space rockets (Figure 7.12).

7.6 The densities of gases

A comparison of the densities of gases will prove crucial in our pursuit of the relative masses of atoms. A density is obtained by dividing a mass by a volume. But with gases, we have seen that the volume we divide by varies a lot with temperature and pressure. We must therefore specify a particular temperature and pressure at which the comparison of densities will be made. Our comparison will be made at the temperature of an ice–water bath, and a pressure of 760 mm (76 cm) of mercury. The chemical symbol of mercury is Hg. The temperature can therefore be written as 0 °C, and the pressure as 760 mmHg. These conditions are often called **standard temperature and pressure**, usually abbreviated to **STP**. They resemble those of a cold, fine English winter's day.

The principles of the density measurement can be illustrated by means of the glass bulb in Figure 7.13. It is fitted with two exit tubes and taps. The internal volume must be known, but this is easily found from the increase in mass when the bulb is filled to the stopcock taps with water.

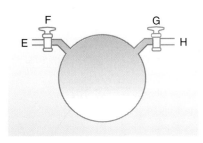

Figure 7.13 A glass bulb suitable for gas density measurements.

○ Water has a density of 1.00 g cm^{-3}. If the increase in mass is 228 g, what is the volume of the bulb?

○ Since density = $\dfrac{\text{mass}}{\text{volume}}$

$$\text{volume} = \frac{\text{mass}}{\text{density}} = \frac{228\ \text{g}}{1.00\ \text{g cm}^{-3}} = 228\ \text{cm}^3$$

The bulb is now emptied and dried. Taps F and G are closed, and a suction pump is attached at H. Tap G is opened, and the air is sucked out. Tap G is now closed, and the bulb is disconnected from the pump and weighed.

Now the bulb is immersed in an ice–water bath. It is then connected, through a plastic sleeve at E, to an oxygen gas supply-line (Figure 7.14). This supply-line includes a T-junction, D, where there is a U-tube of mercury for pressure measurements. Taps A and F are gently opened so that oxygen floods the evacuated bulb. Then tap G is opened as well, so that a stream of oxygen flushes through the bulb. After a few minutes, taps A and G are closed. Now the pressure of the oxygen gas in the bulb can

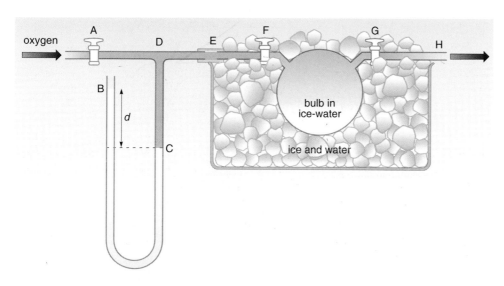

Figure 7.14 The bulb of Figure 7.13, immersed in ice–water and connected to a supply-line, which will allow it to be filled with oxygen at 0 °C and an accurately known pressure.

be measured by using the mercury U-tube. It is equal to the upward pressure from the mercury at C. This is atmospheric pressure (the pressure at B) plus the pressure due to the excess height of mercury, d. Now tap F is closed, the bulb disconnected, and the outside surface dried. Then the final weighing is made.

Table 7.2 Data obtained in an experiment to find the density of oxygen.

mass of bulb with air sucked out	=	141.376 g
mass of bulb + oxygen	=	141.697 g
pressure in bulb	=	750 mmHg
temperature of bulb	=	0 °C
volume of bulb	=	228 cm³

228 cm³ of oxygen at *750* mmHg and *0* °C have a mass of *0.321* g

⬤ A set of possible results is shown in Table 7.2. At the bottom of the table is a sentence that includes four spaces. Pencil numbers into these spaces.

⚪ 228 cm³ of oxygen at a pressure of 750 mmHg and a temperature of 0 °C have a mass of 0.321 g. The oxygen occupies the volume of the bulb and its mass is the difference between the two weighings. Notice that the temperature is that of the ice–water bath (0 °C), even though the final weighing was not made at this temperature. This does not matter, because the mass of oxygen detected by the weighing was *sealed* in the bulb at 0 °C.

So the temperature specified in our sentence is our chosen standard temperature of 0 °C, but the pressure (750 mmHg) is not our chosen standard pressure of 760 mmHg. To correct for this, we ask what the volume of the oxygen would be if it were at 760 mmHg instead of 750 mmHg. Boyle's law tells us that the product of the pressure and the volume is constant at constant temperature. So,

760 mmHg × (volume at 760 mmHg) = 750 mmHg × (volume at 750 mmHg) (7.8)

Table 7.3 Densities of some gases at STP.

Gas	Density /g litre^{-1}
hydrogen	0.089 9
helium	0.179
methane	0.716
ammonia	0.760
carbon monoxide	1.25
nitrogen	1.25
dry air	1.29
ethane	1.34
oxygen	1.43
hydrogen chloride	1.63
carbon dioxide	1.96
propane	1.97
chlorine	3.16

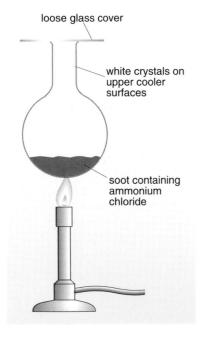

Figure 7.15 Ammonium chloride that is mixed with soot can be separated by sublimation. The mixture is heated; it fumes, and the fumes are reconstituted as white crystals of ammonium chloride on a cooled surface above.

Now the volume at 750 mmHg is 228 cm^3. If we substitute this, and divide both sides of the equation by 760 mmHg:

$$\text{volume at 760 mmHg} = \frac{750\,\text{mmHg} \times 228\,\text{cm}^3}{760\,\text{mmHg}} = 225\,\text{cm}^3 \qquad (7.9)$$

Note that one of the units (mmHg) cancels on the top and bottom of the fraction. We can now rewrite our sentence using the abbreviation STP for the conditions of 760 mmHg pressure and 0 °C: we can say that 225 cm^3 of oxygen at STP have a mass of 0.321 g.

○ What is the mass of 1 000 cm^3 of oxygen at STP?

○ mass of 225 cm^3 of oxygen at STP = 0.321 g

$$\text{mass of 1 000 cm}^3 \text{ of oxygen at STP} = \frac{1000 \times 0.321\,\text{g}}{225} = 1.43\,\text{g}$$

Since 1 000 cm^3 is one litre, one litre of oxygen at STP has a mass of 1.43 g. So the density of oxygen at STP is 1.43 g litre^{-1}.

In Table 7.3, we list in ascending order the densities at STP of a number of gases. They include air, which is, of course, a mixture. Take a look at the values.

○ During this block we have noted that hydrogen can lift balloons, that the coal pit fireman hugged the ground as the wild fire he had ignited swept along the roof, that hydrogen chloride is collected by upward displacement of air, that Mr Reeder's captive assassin could have stored carbon dioxide but not carbon monoxide in jugs, and that chlorine was used as a war gas. Are these observations compatible with Table 7.3?

○ They are; they require hydrogen and methane to be less dense than air and hydrogen chloride, chlorine and carbon dioxide but not carbon monoxide to be substantially more dense than air. This is the case.

7.7 The eagle in the dung heap: ammonium chloride and ammonia

Table 7.3 includes data on ammonia, a compound that will be useful to us in our hunt for reliable relative atomic masses. Hundreds of years ago, a new white solid was imported into Europe from the East. Some called it *the white eagle*. This was because if a surface on which it lay was strongly heated, the white solid took wing in a cloud of fumes, and then reconstituted itself on a cooler surface above (Figure 7.15). This ability of a heated solid to pass directly to the vapour state without melting is called *sublimation*. The new substance was ammonium chloride, and it came from Egypt where it had been sublimed from the soot of furnaces that had been fired with camel dung. It was found most useful for cleaning metals, and to make it themselves, Europeans fell back on various combinations of urine, salt and soot. The morning urine of 10-year-old boys was said to be especially efficacious. It is perhaps best to pass over this observation in silence, but whatever the reactants, any ammonium chloride that was produced was separated and purified by exploiting its willingness to sublime.

Ammonia is a gas that can be made (Figure 7.16) by heating ammonium chloride either with quicklime (calcium oxide), or with calcium hydroxide, a white solid obtained by adding water to quicklime.

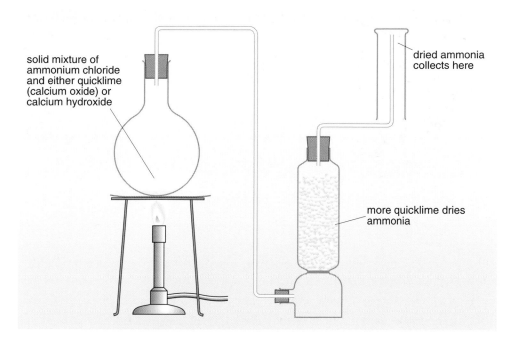

solid mixture of ammonium chloride and either quicklime (calcium oxide) or calcium hydroxide

dried ammonia collects here

more quicklime dries ammonia

Figure 7.16 Making ammonia: the gas is dried in the tower of quicklime, which absorbs water (Section 5). Quicklime is used because more familiar drying agents, such as calcium chloride or sulfuric acid, react with ammonia.

● Is ammonia more or less dense than air?

○ Less dense: in Figure 7.16, it is collected by downward displacement of air. This agrees with the density value in Table 7.3.

Ammonia is immensely soluble in water, and, unlike acids, which turn blue litmus red, the solution turns red litmus blue. Both these properties are demonstrated in Figure 7.17. The solution is used in household cleaning materials and smells of the gas; consequently, you will probably be familiar with its intense, pungent smell. Ammonia gas produces thick, white fumes if it is brought into contact with hydrogen chloride. This is because the two gases react to produce solid particles of ammonium chloride:

ammonia + hydrogen chloride $\longrightarrow$ ammonium chloride (7.10)

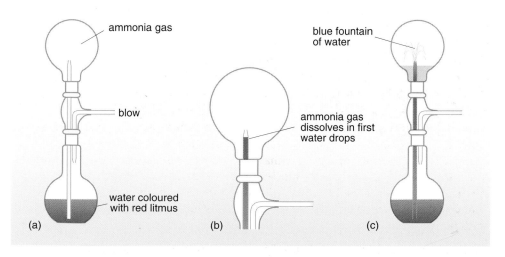

ammonia gas

blow

water coloured with red litmus

(a)

ammonia gas dissolves in first water drops

(b)

blue fountain of water

(c)

Figure 7.17 The fountain experiment illustrates the high solubility of ammonia. (a) An inverted flask full of ammonia is connected by a tube to another flask containing a solution of litmus in water that has been coloured red with a trace of acid. By blowing down the auxiliary tube, this water is forced up the connecting tube into the ammonia. (b) Because ammonia is so soluble, the first few drops of water dissolve the entire contents of the flask, leaving a vacuum. (c) Drawn by the vacuum, water then fountains in without further assistance, nearly filling the inverted flask. As it enters, the ammonia turns the red litmus blue.

Ammonia is composed of the elements nitrogen and hydrogen. When ammonia gas is passed over hot copper oxide, its hydrogen is converted into water, and uncombined nitrogen is left as a gas:

$$\text{ammonia + copper oxide} \longrightarrow \text{nitrogen + water + copper} \tag{7.11}$$

In Activity 6.1, you determined the chemical composition of methane through its reaction with copper oxide; reaction 7.11 allows us to do the same for ammonia. We shall not go into details, but merely quote the results: the composition of ammonia is 82.2% nitrogen and 17.8% hydrogen. Let's use these results to remind ourselves of the vital problem that we have to solve. What they tell us is that in 100 g of ammonia:

17.8 g of hydrogen are combined with 82.2 g of nitrogen

1.00 g of hydrogen is combined with $\frac{82.2}{17.8}$ g of nitrogen

This tells us that, in ammonia, every 1.00 g of hydrogen is combined with 4.62 g of nitrogen. Now suppose that the chemical formula of the ammonia molecule is NH.

⬤ What would be the ratio of the mass of a nitrogen atom to that of a hydrogen atom?

◯ As 4.62 g of nitrogen and 1.00 g of hydrogen would then contain the same number of atoms, the ratio would be 4.62 : 1.

But on the other hand, if the formula of ammonia were NH_2, the mass of a nitrogen atom would then be 9.24 times the mass of a hydrogen atom: 4.62 g of nitrogen and 0.5 g of hydrogen would contain the same number of atoms. Until we can figure out correct chemical formulae, we shall not be able to get reliable relative atomic masses.

7.8 Gay-Lussac's law

One more piece of the jig-saw is needed before we put the whole thing together in Section 8. So far we have concentrated on the *masses* of substances that combine in chemical reactions, and these do not, in general, react in simple ratios. For example, when 1.00 g of hydrogen forms hydrogen chloride, it combines with 35.2 g of chlorine (Activity 4.1). But our study of gas densities now allows us to compare the combining *volumes* of gases. What sort of ratios do these combine in?

Let's look at the reaction of hydrogen and oxygen to form water. Water is 11.2% hydrogen and 88.8% oxygen, so 0.112 g of hydrogen will combine with 0.888 g of oxygen to form 1.000 g of water.

⬤ Use the densities in Table 7.3 to calculate the volumes of 0.112 g of hydrogen and 0.888 g of oxygen at STP.

◯ At STP, 0.089 9 g of hydrogen occupies 1 litre, so 0.112 g occupies $\frac{0.112}{0.089\,9}$ or 1.25 litres. At STP, 1.43 g of oxygen occupy 1 litre, so 0.888 g occupies $\frac{0.888}{1.43}$ or 0.621 litre.

These volumes of hydrogen and oxygen (1.25 litres and 0.621 litre) are in a ratio of almost exactly 2 : 1. And this is not just an abstract exercise; the electrical decomposition of water (Figure 3.9) breaks water down into volumes of hydrogen and oxygen that are in this ratio. Moreover, the double volume of hydrogen that is produced recombines exactly with the single volume of oxygen when the gases are reconverted (Figure 3.10) into water. We conclude therefore, that when 0.112 g of hydrogen combines with 0.888 g of oxygen at STP, the combining volumes are 1.25 and 0.621 litres, which are in the ratio 2 : 1.

Now let us imagine that the 1.000 g of water that the gases produce is in the gaseous state. What would be *its* volume? You may argue that this is a ridiculous question: at STP (760 mmHg and 0 °C) water might be solid or liquid, but it will not be a gas. Nevertheless, the gas laws that we have developed in this section allow us to say what the volume would be if a gas could be got. In Figure 7.9 we found that at 760 mmHg pressure and 200 °C, 1 g of water has a volume of 2.16 litres. In Section 7.4, we used Charles' law to show that if the pressure is kept constant, the volume of a gas at 0 °C is $\frac{273}{473}$, or 57.7%, of its volume at 200 °C.

○ What would be the predicted volume of 1 g of gaseous water at 760 mmHg and 0 °C? Is it a simple multiple of the volumes of the hydrogen and oxygen that would combine, at STP, to form 1 g of water?

○ The predicted volume is 1.25 litres (57.7% of 2.16 litres). This volume is produced by the combination of 1.25 litres of hydrogen and 0.621 litre of oxygen. So the volumes of gaseous water, hydrogen and oxygen are in the ratio 2 : 2 : 1.

Thus, when water is formed from hydrogen and oxygen at STP, every volume of oxygen combines with twice its volume of hydrogen, and, if gaseous water were formed, would yield twice its volume of water vapour:

2 volumes hydrogen + 1 volume oxygen ⟶ 2 volumes water vapour   (7.12)

This is just one instance of a law discovered by the French chemist, Joseph Gay-Lussac (Figure 7.18).

> If the volumes in which gases react are measured at the same temperature and pressure, they turn out to be in a simple ratio to one another, and to the volume of the product, if it is also gaseous.

We have demonstrated **Gay-Lussac's law** by *calculating* the volumes that react and appear when water is formed from its elements. If you find direct observation more convincing, Figure 7.19 shows how such volumes can almost be *seen* when hydrogen chloride is formed from hydrogen and chlorine. Read the figure caption. We shall call the volume of vessel B one *volume unit*.

Figure 7.18 The life of the Frenchman Joseph Gay-Lussac (1778–1850) recalls a more robust age when risks and discovery were regarded as inseparable companions. In 1804, his studies of the atmosphere led to a lone balloon ascent to 7 016 m (23 000 feet), a world altitude record that stood for 50 years. In 1808, he was temporarily blinded by a potassium explosion, and short-term paralysis of the arms resulted from his work on electrical batteries. Three years later, his hands and feet were severely burnt by hot concentrated sulfuric acid. Today's safety officer would have found him a walking nightmare but, as one of his contemporaries said, such people 'had a world to conquer, and would not have traded places with the Persian Shah'.

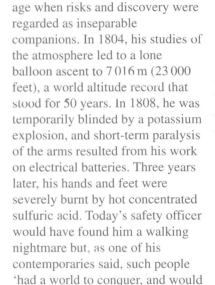

Figure 7.19 Gay-Lussac's law demonstrated by the formation of hydrogen chloride. Vessel A between taps X and Y has twice the volume of vessel B between taps Y and Z. Vessel A contains hydrogen, and vessel B chlorine, both gases being at atmospheric pressure. Tap Y is opened to allow mixing, and the hydrogen and chlorine slowly react together. When the reaction is over, tap Y is left open, and tap Z is opened with its exit tube under the surface of some *mercury*. No gas bubbles out, and no mercury is sucked in. If tap Z is then closed, and tap X is opened with its exit tube under *water*, water is sucked in and just fills vessel A. The remaining gas in B is hydrogen. The temperature is constant.

● Before the reaction in Figure 7.19 begins, how many volume units of hydrogen and chlorine are there?

○ Two volume units of hydrogen in A, and one volume unit of chlorine in B. This is three volume units in all.

When tap Z is opened under mercury, nothing is sucked in and nothing bubbles out so the pressure is unchanged, and the apparatus still contains three volume units of gas at atmospheric pressure. The hydrogen chloride in this gas can be detected by using its great solubility in water (Figure 2.14); when tap X is opened under water, all the hydrogen chloride dissolves in the water, which rushes in and replaces it.

● So what was the composition of the gas, in volume units, before tap X was opened under water?

○ Vessel A was filled with water, leaving vessel B full of hydrogen. That means that there were two volume units of hydrogen chloride and one of hydrogen.

If we compare the initial and final situations, one volume unit of hydrogen and one volume unit of chlorine have been consumed, and two volume units of hydrogen chloride have been produced. The gases hydrogen and chlorine have clearly reacted in volumes that bear a simple ratio to each other, and to the volume of the gaseous product.

7.9   Summary of Section 7

Figure 7.20   A reaction flow diagram showing some of the new chemical reactions that you met in Section 7.

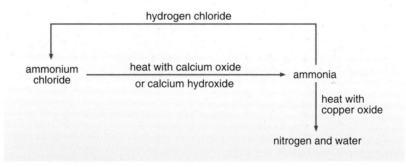

New chemical reactions that you met in Section 7 are summarized in Figure 7.20; ammonia is a compound of nitrogen and hydrogen. The essential points of the section are:

1   Pressure in a liquid increases with depth, and at any point in the liquid is transmitted equally in all directions. If there is some uninterrupted pathway through the liquid, however indirect, between two points at the same horizontal level, the pressure at the two points is the same.

2   The Earth's atmosphere exerts a pressure like other fluids. One measure of that pressure is the height of the mercury column that it will support in an arrangement like Figure 7.3c. At sea-level, this is about 76 cm or 760 mm.

3   At everyday pressures, gases have very low densities, and in sealed vessels at a fixed temperature, the pressure does not change significantly with height and is the same throughout. This pressure can be measured by connecting the vessel to a glass U-tube containing mercury (Figure 7.14).

4   At constant temperature, the pressure of a fixed mass of gas multiplied by its volume is a constant. This is Boyle's law (PV = constant).

5   At constant pressure, the volume of a fixed mass of gas divided by its absolute temperature is a constant. This is Charles' law ($\frac{V}{T}$ = constant).

6   Many properties of gases can be understood by using a model in which the gas is thought of as a collection of tiny particles in constant motion. These tiny particles are called molecules. They collide with the walls of the container, and with each other. Gas pressure is the result of the incessant drumming of the molecules on the containing walls; a rise in temperature increases the average speed of the molecules.

7   Gas densities are determined by evacuating a bulb of known volume, weighing it, filling it with the gas at a known temperature and pressure, and weighing it again. A meaningful comparison of gas densities is possible only at the same temperature and pressure. We made this comparison at STP, a pressure of 760 mmHg and a temperature of 0 °C.

8   If the volumes in which gases react are measured at the same temperature and pressure, they turn out to be in a simple ratio to one another, and to the volume of the product, if it is also gaseous. This is Gay-Lussac's law. For example,

2 volumes hydrogen + 1 volume oxygen $\longrightarrow$ 2 volumes water vapour

1 volume hydrogen + 1 volume chlorine $\longrightarrow$ 2 volumes hydrogen chloride

In Section 7, we began with pressure in liquids, and especially within columns and U-tubes of mercury, because this enables us to determine the pressure of a gas. Points 1–3 summarize the essentials, and Questions 7.1–7.3 test your understanding of them.

Points 4 and 5 summarize the variation of the volume of a confined gas with pressure and temperature. They allow you to correct the volume of a gas at some given pressure and temperature to a pressure of 760 mmHg and a temperature of 0 °C (i.e. to STP). Question 7.4 tests you on this, but notice that the essentials of the calculation have already been covered in Activity 7.2. Calculations on gases are also involved in points 7 and 8. At a particular temperature and pressure, the density of a gas is obtained by dividing the mass of a fixed amount of the gas by its volume. You can calculate any one of the three quantities — mass, volume and density — when you are told the other two. This operation is involved in Question 7.5, which makes a further test of Gay-Lussac's law.

Question 7.1   Pascal repeated the Torricelli experiment of Figure 7.3 using water in place of mercury. Would you expect the height of the column of water in the sealed tube to be greater or less than that of the column of mercury? The density of mercury is 13.6 times that of water. On a day when the atmospheric pressure is 760 mmHg what would the height of the water column be? ◀

Question 7.2   Look again at Kapitan-Leutnant Wenniger's description of his escape from UB-55 (Box 7.1).

(a) Wenniger says that 'eventually' he was able to open the conning tower hatch. Why 'eventually'?

(b) Why did he find himself forced to exhale during his ascent?

(c) Why did he find his lifejacket inflated when he reached the surface?

(d) What do you think killed the men who broke surface, screamed and then sank?

(e) The pressure at a depth of 40 metres will be greater than the atmospheric pressure at the surface. Use the answer to Question 7.1 to find out approximately how much greater. ◀

Question 7.3 Figures 7.21a–c show a gas in a sealed bulb connected to a mercury U-tube. If the atmospheric pressure is 760 mmHg, what is the pressure of the gas in each case? ◀

Figure 7.21 For use with Question 7.3.

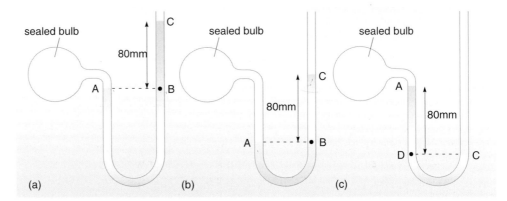

Question 7.4 A gas sample has a volume of 760 cm³ at a temperature of 100 °C and a pressure of 1 000 mmHg. What would the sample volume be at a temperature of 0 °C and a pressure of 760 mmHg? ◀

Question 7.5 Figure 7.19 showed how the combining volumes of hydrogen and chlorine, and the volume of the hydrogen chloride product, can be observed in an experiment. But these volumes can also be calculated from the chemical composition of hydrogen chloride (H, 2.76%; Cl, 97.2%) that you obtained in Activity 4.1. This tells you that 0.027 6 g of hydrogen combines with 0.972 g of chlorine to give 1.000 g of hydrogen chloride. Use the densities listed in Table 7.3 to calculate the volumes of these three masses of gas at STP. Are they in the expected ratio? ◀

The Italian job

8

We now have the data and the concepts that we need to work out a scale of relative atomic masses, and to calculate the chemical formulae of methane and many other compounds. The way forward was first revealed by two clever Italians who grappled with the problem in the 19th century.

8.1 Avogadro's hypothesis

Let's start with Gay-Lussac's law. One example of the law was the reaction between hydrogen and chlorine. In the experiment of Figure 7.19, we found that:

1 volume hydrogen + 1 volume chlorine $\longrightarrow$ 2 volumes hydrogen chloride (8.1)

Thus at a particular temperature and pressure, hydrogen chloride is formed by the combination of equal volumes of hydrogen and chlorine. Now hydrogen and chlorine are gases: they contain molecules. Also, the atomic theory that we introduced in Section 6 assumes that atoms and molecules combine or react together in simple ratios. What this means in this case is that the numbers of molecules in the equal volumes of hydrogen and chlorine that react, must stand in a simple ratio to one another. To make sure that you understand this, you should now try Activity 8.1.

Activity 8.1 Deducing the different consequences of competing hypotheses

This activity will help you to understand why the conclusion reached at the end of the last paragraph is an inevitable consequence of the atomic theory and Gay-Lussac's law. ◀

So Activity 8.1, and other examples of Gay-Lussac's law, drive us to the inescapable conclusion that there are simple numerical ratios between the numbers of molecules in equal volumes of different gases, when these volumes are set at the same temperature and pressure. But how can we decide what these simple ratios are? In 1811, an Italian physicist, Amadeo Avogadro, suggested that the second sentence that you completed for hydrogen and chlorine in Figure 8.1.1 in Activity 8.1 is true for *all* gases: the ratio is always 1 : 1. Whatever the gas, the number of molecules in a particular volume is always the same:

Under the same conditions of temperature and pressure, equal volumes of different gases contain the same number of molecules.

We shall call this proposal **Avogadro's hypothesis**. Figure 8.1 provides you with a picture of it by using our model of a gas.

Figure 8.1 Two containers with the same volume but containing different gases. The gas on the left has smaller and less massive molecules than that on the right. Both gases are at the same temperature and pressure. In agreement with Avogadro's hypothesis, there is the same number of molecules in each container (count them). It follows that the average distance between the centres of the molecules is the same in both gases, even though the molecules of one gas are different from those of the other.

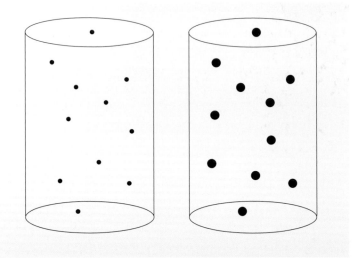

So what Avogadro's hypothesis suggests is that, in different gases at the same temperature and pressure, the average distance between the molecules is the same. That average distance depends on the temperature and pressure alone, and not on the nature of the gas molecules themselves.

Avogadro's hypothesis is attractive because it is the *simplest* of the options that can explain Gay-Lussac's law. This alone cannot be convincing, but it does suggest that the idea is worth following up. Science often proceeds in this way. For the moment, the proposal is a tentative one: indeed, this is why it is described as a *hypothesis.** It is an exciting idea, and we go forward with it in the hope that the evidence in its favour will grow stronger.

8.1.1 Some consequences of Avogadro's hypothesis

Equation 8.1 tells us that:

1 volume hydrogen + 1 volume chlorine ⟶ 2 volumes hydrogen chloride (8.1)

Suppose that, as in Activity 8.1, the one volume of chlorine contains 10 billion chlorine molecules, and that Avogadro's hypothesis is true.

● How many hydrogen molecules react with the 10 billion chlorine molecules, and how many hydrogen chloride molecules will then be formed?

○ Avogadro's hypothesis tells us that the equal volumes of hydrogen and chlorine that react contain the same number of molecules. The double volume of hydrogen chloride that is formed must contain twice that number. So 10 billion hydrogen molecules will react with the 10 billion chlorine molecules to generate 20 billion hydrogen chloride molecules.

Now if 10 billion hydrogen molecules react with 10 billion chlorine molecules to give 20 billion hydrogen chloride molecules, then every hydrogen molecule reacts with one chlorine molecule to give two hydrogen chloride molecules:

1 molecule hydrogen + 1 molecule chlorine ⟶ 2 molecules hydrogen chloride (8.2)

---

* Today, the evidence in its favour is much stronger and it is often called Avogadro's *law.*

○ Now compare Equations 8.1 and 8.2. How do they differ?

○ The only change is that the word 'volume' in Equation 8.1 has been replaced by the word 'molecule' in Equation 8.2.

This is one of the agreeable consequences of Avogadro's hypothesis. When we have an example of Gay-Lussac's law like Equation 8.1, then the statement remains true when we replace volumes by molecules. Our other example of Gay-Lussac's law was:

2 volumes hydrogen + 1 volume oxygen ⟶ 2 volumes water vapour   (8.3)

○ Rewrite this equation to reveal the ratios between the reactant and product molecules.

○ 2 molecules hydrogen + 1 molecule oxygen ⟶ 2 molecules water vapour (8.4)

Equations 8.2 and 8.4 are consequences of Avogadro's hypothesis, but they reveal a very important difficulty. Think about the oxygen molecule in Equation 8.4. Suppose that this molecule, one of the tiny particles of which oxygen gas is made, is a *single oxygen atom*. Consider what happens to it in the reaction.

○ What difficulty then arises?

○ The single atom that appears on the left of the equation must be *divided* between the two molecules of water on the right. The dividing of atoms is forbidden by proposition 1 of our atomic theory (Section 6).

Avogadro did not like this either, and he had an answer to the problem. He suggested that the molecules of gaseous elements such as hydrogen, chlorine and oxygen *contain more than one atom*. Now in Block 2, you were told, without proof, that the oxygen molecules in the atmosphere contain *two* oxygen atoms. They can therefore be written O_2. This formula fits Equation 8.4 without violating the atomic theory: it is now an O_2 molecule that is divided between the two water molecules; each of its oxygen atoms goes into a separate water molecule without division.

○ But is the molecular formula O_2 the only one that avoids violating the atomic theory?

○ No; as Avogadro saw, any molecular formula containing an *even number* of oxygen atoms avoids the division of atoms. O_4, O_6, etc. are equally acceptable.

Even now, we cannot assign chemical formulae with complete confidence.

8.2   The Karlsruhe conference

You can't get the chemical formulae until you know the relative atomic masses, and you can't get the relative atomic masses until you know the chemical formulae. This problem is taking us some time to solve, but this is not surprising because the scientists who first turned their minds to it took 50 years to do the job. The problem was seen as soon as Dalton published his atomic theory in 1807, but despite the appearance of Avogadro's hypothesis just four years later, it remained unsolved. Scientists became desperate and did something that had never been done before: they called an international meeting to try to reach an agreement.

Figure 8.2 Stanislao Cannizzaro (1826–1910) was a Sicilian who combined chemistry with revolutionary activity in the struggles that led to a united, independent Italy. In 1849, he fled to France after the failure of a rebellion in which he served as an artillery officer. He slipped back to Italy in 1851, becoming Professor at Genoa where he wrote the famous Karlsruhe pamphlet. He later joined another rebellion in Sicily, where he enjoyed the experience of arriving too late for the fighting, but in time to join the new government.

The event was held at Karlsruhe in Germany in 1860. About 140 people turned up. Among them was the composer Borodin, who had studied chemistry in St Petersburg. On the first evening, he played the piano at the banquet and sang *The Volga Boatman* with a scruffy-looking young Russian called Mendeléev. But both of them were to be upstaged by a 34-year-old Italian named Stanislao Cannizzaro (Figure 8.2). When the real business of the conference began, many of the contributors made rambling, futile speeches. Cannizzaro was not like that; here was a man with a mission. Not only had he prepared what he wanted to say, but he carried copies of a pamphlet that set out his detailed arguments. His speech went down well, but not well enough, and the conference broke up without agreement. But as it did so, a friend of Cannizzaro's handed out copies of the pamphlet. The effect on some of the key participants was profound. The German, Lothar Meyer, read it in the train on the way home:

> I read it again and again, and was astonished at the insights that this little paper gave me into the problems that had troubled us. The scales fell from my eyes, doubts disappeared, and a feeling of calm certainty reigned in their place.

What was there in Cannizzaro's pamphlet that could produce so profound an effect?

8.3 Cannizzaro's principle

The argument that now follows was one of the most influential in the whole of science. Cannizzaro begins it by telling us that he intends to use Avogadro's hypothesis to the fullest possible extent. This is a typically bold move because the evidence in its favour is not strong. The hypothesis is, however, the *simplest* of the ones that can explain Gay-Lussac's law and, other things being equal, science has an in-built prejudice that favours the simple over the complex. As other things seem to be equal, let us give Cannizzaro his head.

He turns to the densities of gases; a selection of such densities for hydrogen and six of its gaseous compounds appears in column 2 of Table 8.1.

Table 8.1 The calculation of the number of hydrogen atoms in the molecules of some gases using Cannizzaro's principle. N is the number of molecules in 1 litre of a gas at STP.

Gas	Density at STP/g litre^{-1}	Mass of molecule/g	Percentage of hydrogen by mass/%	Mass of hydrogen per molecule/g	Previous column divided by hydrogen chloride value
hydrogen	0.089 9	$\frac{0.089\ 9}{N}$	100	$\frac{0.089\ 9}{N}$	2.00
methane	0.716	$\frac{0.716}{N}$	25.1	$\frac{0.180}{N}$	4.00
ammonia	0.760	$\frac{0.760}{N}$	17.8	$\frac{0.135}{N}$	3.00
water vapour	0.804	$\frac{0.804}{N}$	11.2	$\frac{0.090\ 0}{N}$	2.00
ethane	1.34	$\frac{1.34}{N}$	20.1	$\frac{0.269}{N}$	5.98
hydrogen chloride	1.63	$\frac{1.63}{N}$	2.76	$\frac{0.045\ 0}{N}$	1.00
propane	1.97	$\frac{1.97}{N}$	18.3	$\frac{0.360}{N}$	8.00

They tell us the mass (in grams) of each substance in a volume of 1 litre at STP. Thus for methane at STP, 1 litre contains 0.716 g. Now according to Avogadro's hypothesis, the volumes of 1 litre of the different gases at STP must all contain the *same* number of molecules. Let us use algebra, and call this number of molecules in 1 litre, N. We do not know the size of N. No doubt it will be large because molecules are very small, but the important thing is that it is the same for the different gases.

○ What is the mass of one molecule of methane?

○ There is 0.716 g of methane in 1 litre at STP. The number of methane molecules in one litre is N. Each molecule therefore has a mass of $\frac{0.716}{N}$ g (Figure 8.3).

Help needed? If you do not like using a letter N for the number of molecules in 1 litre of gas at STP, use any fixed number of your choice; for example, one billion. Then, for example, the mass of a methane molecule is 0.716 billionths of a gram. So long as *you* use the same number whenever *we* use N, the logic of the argument remains sound. Cannizzaro himself advised his own students to do this.

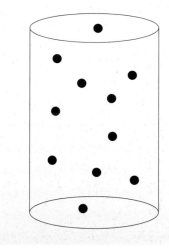

Figure 8.3 If a container encloses N molecules of a gas, then the mass of one molecule is the total mass of gas in the container divided by N. In this case, $N = 11$, so each molecule has a mass which is one-eleventh of the total mass of gas in the container.

In column 3 of Table 8.1, the masses of the molecules of all seven gases appear in this form. Now we calculate the mass of hydrogen in these molecular masses. To do this, we use the chemical compositions of the substances that we obtained in Sections 3.5, 6.5, 7.7 and in Activity 4.1. From these compositions comes the percentage of hydrogen by mass in each substance. These appear in column 4.

○ Why is the value for hydrogen 100%?

○ Hydrogen is an element: in the gas, the molecules, however many hydrogen atoms they contain, are composed just of hydrogen atoms. Thus hydrogen gas is 100% hydrogen.

Methane, however, is a compound and, as Section 6.5 showed, contains only 25.1% hydrogen by mass.

○ If the mass of a methane molecule is $\frac{0.716}{N}$ g, how can the mass of hydrogen in that molecule be found?

○ By multiplying $\frac{0.716}{N}$ g by $\frac{25.1}{100}$. Methane is composed of identical molecules so each molecule has the composition of methane itself: 25.1% of the mass of a methane molecule comes from the hydrogen atoms in it.

In column 5 of Table 8.1, the mass of hydrogen in one molecule of each gas has been calculated in this way.

○ Which molecule contains the smallest mass of hydrogen?

○ Hydrogen chloride: it contains only $\frac{0.0450}{N}$ g of hydrogen. All other molecules in the table contain more hydrogen than this; water, for example, contains twice as much ($\frac{0.0900}{N}$ g).

Cannizzaro looked at lots of gaseous hydrogen compounds. Nowhere did he find a molecule that contained a mass of hydrogen lower than that in the hydrogen chloride molecule. So he advanced the following proposal, now known as **Cannizzaro's principle**:

> The mass of one atom of an element is the smallest mass of that element found in any molecule containing it.

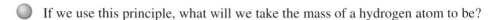 If we use this principle, what will we take the mass of a hydrogen atom to be?

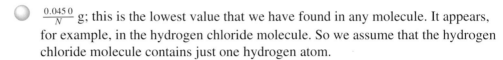 $\frac{0.045\,0}{N}$ g; this is the lowest value that we have found in any molecule. It appears, for example, in the hydrogen chloride molecule. So we assume that the hydrogen chloride molecule contains just one hydrogen atom.

Once this decision has been taken, we can see that the masses of hydrogen in each of the molecules in Table 8.1 are *whole number* multiples of $\frac{0.045\,0}{N}$ g. This is made clear in column 6, where the masses of hydrogen from column 5 have each been divided by $\frac{0.045\,0}{N}$ g: to three significant figures, the results hardly differ from whole numbers. In the molecules of hydrogen, methane, ammonia, water, ethane, hydrogen chloride and propane, the masses of hydrogen are in the ratio $2:4:3:2:6:1:8$.

What does this tell us about the number of hydrogen atoms in the molecules of these gases?

The numbers are 2, 4, 3, 2, 6, 1 and 8, respectively. Since, according to Cannizzaro's principle, the hydrogen chloride molecule contains one hydrogen atom then, as the methane molecule (for example) contains four times as much hydrogen as the molecule of hydrogen chloride, it must contain four hydrogen atoms.

Column 6 of Table 8.1 also tells us that the hydrogen molecule contains *two* hydrogen atoms and not one. We must write it H_2. To give you further help with this argument, Figure 8.4 does it in pictures. We now have evidence that there are four hydrogen atoms in the methane molecule. But how many carbon atoms are there? You can find out by doing Activity 8.2.

Activity 8.2   Counting carbon atoms

You have just been shown how to work out the number of hydrogen atoms in the molecules of hydrogen, methane, ammonia, water, ethane, hydrogen chloride and propane. In this activity you will identify the main steps in the procedure and check your understanding of it by counting the carbon atoms in the molecules of methane, carbon monoxide, ethane, carbon dioxide and propane. ◀

8.3.1   Some chemical formulae

Chemical formulae for the molecules of many substances can be worked out by the methods of Section 8.3 and Activity 8.2. Table 8.2 shows some examples. Notice that the common gases hydrogen, chlorine, nitrogen and oxygen are composed of molecules that contain two atoms. These molecules are therefore said to be *diatomic*. Table 8.2 also shows you that the water molecule is H_2O (it contains one oxygen and two hydrogen atoms), and that our guesses as to the chemical formulae of the carbon oxides in Section 5 were correct: they are CO and CO_2.

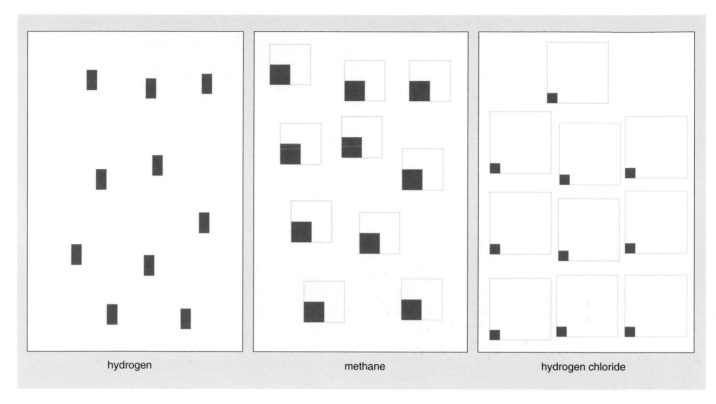

| hydrogen | methane | hydrogen chloride |

Figure 8.4 Cannizzaro's argument in pictures: the boxes show equal volumes of hydrogen, methane and hydrogen chloride at STP. Molecules are shown as rectangles whose areas represent their mass. By Avogadro's hypothesis, the equal volumes contain equal numbers of molecules (here shown as 10) so the ratio of the masses for the different molecules (hydrogen, methane, hydrogen chloride) is the same as that of the gas densities: about $1 : 8 : 18$. So in the figure, the masses of the molecules are represented by rectangles whose areas are in this ratio. The mass of hydrogen in each molecule is then represented by an area whose percentage of the rectangle is equal to the percentage of hydrogen in the compound. These areas, calculated from the hydrogen percentages in Table 8.1, are marked in red. When calculated for hydrogen, methane and hydrogen chloride, they turn out to be in the exact ratio $2 : 4 : 1$. The hydrogen chloride value is the smallest known in any molecule, so we assume that the hydrogen chloride molecule contains just one hydrogen atom. Then the hydrogen molecule must contain two hydrogen atoms, and the methane molecule four hydrogen atoms.

Table 8.2   The chemical formulae of the molecules of some important substances.

Substance	Formula of molecule	Substance	Formula of molecule
hydrogen	H_2	propane	C_3H_8
oxygen	O_2	hydrogen chloride	HCl
nitrogen	N_2	nitric acid	HNO_3
ammonia	NH_3	sulfuric acid	H_2SO_4
water	H_2O	chlorine	Cl_2
carbon monoxide	CO	bromine	Br_2
carbon dioxide	CO_2	iodine	I_2
methane	CH_4	nitrogen dioxide	NO_2
ethane	C_2H_6		

8.3.2 Some relative atomic masses

We can use the chemical formulae of Table 8.2 to work out some relative atomic masses. Table 8.2 tells us that the formula of methane is CH_4: in any sample of methane there is one carbon atom for every four hydrogen atoms. In other words, the number of carbon atoms is one-quarter of the number of hydrogen atoms. Now from Section 6.5, you know that 4.0 g of methane contain 3.0 g of carbon and 1.0 g of hydrogen. Suppose that we call the very large number of hydrogen atoms in 1.0 g of hydrogen *one zillion*.

⬤ Then how many carbon atoms will there be in 3.0 g of carbon?

◯ The number of carbon atoms in the 3.0 g of carbon in 4.0 g of methane must be one-quarter of the number of hydrogen atoms in 1.0 g of hydrogen. So 3.0 g of carbon contain one-quarter of a zillion carbon atoms.

This point is made in Figure 8.5a where, for the purposes of illustration, one zillion is represented by eight!

⬤ So what mass of carbon contains one zillion carbon atoms?

◯ If 3.0 g of carbon contain one-quarter of a zillion carbon atoms, 12 g contains one zillion (Figure 8.5b).

As 12 g of carbon and 1.0 g of hydrogen contain equal numbers of atoms, the mass of a carbon atom must be about 12 times that of a hydrogen atom (Figure 8.5c). The problem that we identified at the end of Section 6 has been solved: from the chemical composition of methane we have derived both the chemical formula of the gas, and the relative atomic masses of carbon and hydrogen.

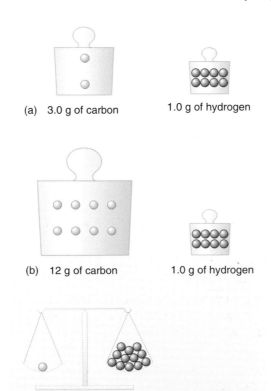

(a) 3.0 g of carbon   1.0 g of hydrogen

(b) 12 g of carbon   1.0 g of hydrogen

(c)

Figure 8.5   Calculating the ratio of the masses of the carbon and hydrogen atoms from the composition and chemical formula of methane (see text). The number called one zillion in the text is here represented by eight.

Question 8.1   In Section 3.2, we found that the chemical composition of water was 88.8% oxygen and 11.2% hydrogen. Work out, to three significant figures, how many grams of oxygen are combined with each gram of hydrogen in water. Then use the chemical formula of water in Table 8.2 to work out, to two significant figures, the relative atomic masses of oxygen and hydrogen.◀

8.4   Summary of Section 8

The essential points of Section 8 are as follows:

1   At the same temperature and pressure, gases react in simple ratios by volume. But the atomic theory suggests that the molecules of which the gases are composed should themselves react in simple numerical ratios. If so, then there must be simple numerical ratios between the numbers of molecules in equal volumes of different gases.

2   Amadeo Avogadro proposed the simplest possible option: at the same temperature and pressure, equal volumes of different gases contain the same number of molecules.

3   If we accept Avogadro's hypothesis, the simple ratios between combining volumes in examples of Gay-Lussac's law become simple ratios in numbers of combining molecules: the word *volume* can be replaced by the word *molecule*.

4   It then follows that the tiny particles (molecules) in hydrogen, chlorine and oxygen gases are not single atoms. The molecules must contain an even number of atoms.

5   Stanislao Cannizzaro used these ideas to obtain both chemical formulae and relative atomic masses. Gas densities for hydrogen and its compounds tell us the mass of each gas in 1 litre at STP. Avogadro's hypothesis tells us that these masses in 1 litre must contain the same number of molecules, N. So the masses of the different molecules can be found by dividing the gas densities by N (column 3 of Table 8.1).

6   By multiplying these masses by the percentage of hydrogen in each compound, the mass of hydrogen in each molecule is obtained (column 5 of Table 8.1). For methane, ammonia, water, hydrogen and hydrogen chloride, respectively, these masses stand in the ratio $4 : 3 : 2 : 2 : 1$.

7   Cannizzaro proposed that the mass of one atom of an element is the *smallest* mass of that element found in any molecule containing it.

8   The mass of hydrogen found in the hydrogen chloride molecule, $\frac{0.045\,0}{N}$ g, is the smallest found in any gaseous compound of hydrogen. This, then, is the mass of a hydrogen atom according to Cannizzaro's principle.

9   Then the molecules of methane, ammonia, water, hydrogen and hydrogen chloride contain 4, 3, 2, 2 and 1 hydrogen atoms, respectively.

10   A similar exercise on gaseous carbon compounds shows that each molecule of methane contains one carbon atom: the chemical formula of methane is CH_4. The chemical composition of methane then sets the ratio between the masses of carbon and hydrogen atoms at $12 : 1$.

The first important operation in Section 8 was the use of Avogadro's hypothesis to find the ratios between the numbers of molecules of gases that are involved in chemical reactions. Questions 8.2 and 8.3 give you the chance to practise this.

In Section 8.3, Cannizzaro's principle was introduced by using it to deduce the number of hydrogen atoms in a set of hydrogen-containing molecules. You were then asked to apply the principle to some carbon-containing molecules in Activity 8.2. Now Activity 8.3 provides you with further practice by asking you to estimate the numbers of oxygen atoms in the molecules of carbon monoxide, carbon dioxide, oxygen, water, sulfur dioxide and ozone.

When you use Cannizzaro's principle in this way, notice how clearly the provisional nature of scientific theory is built into it. In Section 8.3, the mass of the hydrogen atom was taken to be the mass of hydrogen in the hydrogen chloride molecule. This was because this mass is the smallest *so far* found in many experiments on many hydrogen compounds. But Cannizzaro's principle does not preclude the discovery of a new molecule with, say, half this mass of hydrogen in it.

○ If this happened, how would the number of hydrogen atoms in the hydrogen chloride and methane molecules have to be revised to remain consistent with Cannizzaro's principle?

○ They would need to be doubled to two and eight, respectively, because the mass of the hydrogen atom would then be half of what it was before.

This change has never proved necessary, and more recent research provides reasons for thinking that it never will be, but the possibility emphasizes the point made in Box 6.1: science cannot provide final, unalterable certainties.

Another of Cannizzaro's achievements was the clear distinction that he made between atoms and molecules when dealing with gaseous chemical elements. Usually, the molecules, the tiny particles in these gaseous elements that drum against the containing walls and exert pressure, are not single atoms; they consist of two or more atoms of the same type, which are tightly bound together and move about as a single unit. In oxygen, hydrogen, chlorine and nitrogen, the molecules contain two atoms; in ozone, as you will find in Activity 8.3, they contain even more.

Finally, we remind you of the important operation that Cannizzaro's paper made possible: the calculation of a set of relative atomic masses from the chemical formulae that he deduced. In Section 8.3.2 and Question 8.1, the masses of the hydrogen, carbon and oxygen atoms were calculated to be in the approximate ratio $1:12:16$. Question 8.4 gives you the chance to expand this ratio by adding to it data on the mass of the nitrogen atom.

Question 8.2   When carbon monoxide burns in oxygen, it is found that if volumes are measured at the same temperature and pressure, every $10\,cm^3$ of oxygen reacts with $20\,cm^3$ of carbon monoxide to give $20\,cm^3$ of carbon dioxide. Fill in the missing numbers in the spaces in the following equation:

.... volumes carbon monoxide + 1 volume oxygen $\longrightarrow$

.... volumes carbon dioxide

Now use Avogadro's hypothesis to write a similar equation involving molecules rather than volumes. Then rewrite this as a full chemical equation using the chemical formulae in Table 8.2 for the molecules of carbon monoxide, carbon dioxide and oxygen. If these formulae are consistent with the combining volumes and Avogadro's hypothesis, then this equation should be balanced. Is this so? ◀

Question 8.3   Use the formulae in Table 8.2 to write a balanced chemical equation for the decomposition of *two* molecules of ammonia into nitrogen and hydrogen. Ammonia can be decomposed into its elements by electrical sparking (Figure 8.6). When decomposition is over, the gas volume is double what it was before, and three-quarters of this volume is hydrogen, and one-quarter is nitrogen. Explain why your equation accounts for the volume changes that occur in the reaction. ◀

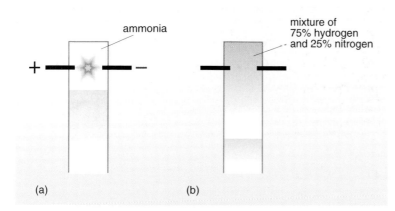

ammonia

mixture of
75% hydrogen
and 25% nitrogen

(a)   (b)

Figure 8.6   (a) Ammonia trapped over mercury is decomposed to nitrogen and hydrogen by electric sparks. (b) When the decomposition is over, the mercury has retreated, and the trapped gas is a mixture of nitrogen and hydrogen which, if the temperature and pressure are unchanged, has twice the volume of its parent ammonia.

Question 8.4   Section 7.7 showed that, in ammonia, each gram of hydrogen was combined with 4.6 g of nitrogen. Use the chemical formula of ammonia to calculate, to two significant figures, the ratio of the masses of the nitrogen and hydrogen atoms. ◀

Activity 8.3   Counting oxygen atoms

In this activity you can find out the formulae of some molecules containing oxygen atoms, including that of ozone — a gas that is often in the news. Ozone is an alternative form of the element oxygen — it contains only oxygen atoms. ◀

9

Revisiting equation-balancing

We have now found a way of determining the chemical formulae of substances from their chemical compositions, and we have a table of such formulae to prove it (Table 8.2). Let's revisit equation-balancing, using some examples in which these formulae appear.

9.1 The flame of burning hydrogen

Hydrogen can be burnt in oxygen in a controlled way (Figure 3.10), but the reaction may also be explosive, as the destruction of the *Hindenburg* (Figure 2.20) showed. Figure 9.1 reminds you of a more recent catastrophe.

In all cases, hydrogen burns in oxygen to give water vapour. From Table 8.2, these substances consist of H_2, O_2 and H_2O molecules, respectively. Usually the hydrogen and oxygen are gases, and so this reaction can be written as:

$$H_2(g) + O_2(g) \longrightarrow H_2O(g) \tag{9.1}$$

◯ Is this equation balanced?

◯ No; there is only one oxygen atom on the right, and there are two on the left.

You can set this right by placing a 2 in front of the water molecule:

$$H_2(g) + O_2(g) \longrightarrow 2H_2O(g) \tag{9.2}$$

◯ Is the equation balanced now?

◯ It is balanced with respect to oxygen, but not with respect to hydrogen. There are four hydrogen atoms on the right, but only two on the left.

Putting a 2 in front of the H_2 molecule on the left corrects this imbalance:

$$2H_2(g) + O_2(g) \longrightarrow 2H_2O(g) \tag{9.3}$$

There are now four hydrogen atoms and two oxygen atoms on each side: the equation is balanced. Two molecules of hydrogen react with one of oxygen to give two molecules of water.

9.2 The flame of natural gas

The combustion of natural gas (Figure 6.7), which is also our coal miner's 'wild fire' (Box 6.2), mainly involves the burning of methane, CH_4, in oxygen, O_2, to give carbon dioxide and water vapour:

$$CH_4(g) + O_2(g) \longrightarrow CO_2(g) + H_2O(g) \tag{9.4}$$

This is balanced with respect to carbon atoms, but not to either hydrogen or oxygen atoms. Skill in equation balancing comes only with practice. We shall start with a particular type of atom, and the job is made easier if you choose wisely. Here it makes sense to leave oxygen atoms until the end — you will see why in a moment. So let us start with the carbon and hydrogen atoms in the molecule of methane on the left.

Figure 9.1 At blast-off, the American space shuttle sits on top of a huge rocket powered by a liquid hydrogen–liquid oxygen propellant. To left and right are the prominent solid fuel booster rockets which are jettisoned after 127 seconds. On 28 January 1986, a ring-seal on the right-hand booster failed, and a sideways flame played upon, then ruptured and ignited the main hydrogen fuel tank. Space shuttle *Challenger* blew up 73 seconds into the flight, and the crew of seven died.

○ The one molecule of methane on the left contains one carbon atom and four hydrogen atoms. So how many carbon dioxide molecules and how many water molecules must there be on the right?

○ The one carbon atom in methane is covered by one molecule of CO_2; the four hydrogen atoms in methane are covered by two molecules of H_2O.

Thus, our first improved equation is:

$$CH_4(g) + O_2(g) \longrightarrow CO_2(g) + 2H_2O(g) \tag{9.5}$$

This is balanced with respect to carbon and hydrogen atoms.

○ What number must you insert, and where, to balance the oxygen atoms?

○ You need a 2 before the O_2 molecule on the left. This gives four oxygen atoms on the left to match the four on the right (two in the CO_2 molecule and one in each of the two H_2O molecules).

The balanced equation is therefore:

$$CH_4(g) + 2O_2(g) \longrightarrow CO_2(g) + 2H_2O(g) \tag{9.6}$$

It made sense to leave the oxygen atoms to the end because oxygen occurs on the left in an uncombined state. *Any* even number of oxygen atoms on the right could then be balanced by just putting the appropriate number before the O_2 molecule on the left.

Question 9.1   Produce balanced equations for the following chemical reactions, including symbols for the states of the different substances.

(a) Solid copper is heated in oxygen gas and forms black copper oxide, CuO (Section 3.2).

(b) Carbon monoxide burns in oxygen with a blue flame and forms carbon dioxide (Section 5.2).

(c) Ammonia is heated with black copper oxide, CuO. Nitrogen, liquid water and copper are then formed (Section 7.7).

(d) Propane, C_3H_8, a minor ingredient of natural gas, burns in oxygen to give carbon dioxide and water vapour. ◀

10 Relative atomic masses

Relative atomic masses have no unit; they are just numbers, one for each chemical element. For any two chemical elements, the ratio between these numbers is the same as the ratio between the masses of their atoms. The set, or scale, of numbers must be fixed by choosing a value for one particular element: we, for example, have worked with the value of 1.0 for hydrogen. In Section 8, we determined some relative masses. Because we wanted you to concentrate on the arguments, and not to get distracted by the arithmetic, we worked with numbers that were given to only two significant figures. Thus we found that, on a scale of relative atomic masses where hydrogen is given the value 1.0, carbon, nitrogen and oxygen have the values 12, 14 and 16, respectively.

Now, the experimental data that we used in setting up this scale consisted of masses and volumes of substances. These can be determined to much higher levels of accuracy than two significant figures; so also, therefore, can the scale of relative atomic masses. Column 2 of Table 10.1, for example, shows values for some common elements, on the scale that we have used so far, to *three* significant figures. This scale, therefore, now becomes one on which hydrogen is given the value 1.00. Look at the values that are presented in Table 10.1 under the heading H = 1.00.

Table 10.1 Some relative atomic masses, given to three significant figures; first, in column 2, on a scale in which H = 1.00; then, in column 3, on a scale in which O = 16.0.

Element	Relative atomic mass	
	H = 1.00	O = 16.0
hydrogen	1.00	1.01
carbon	11.9	12.0
nitrogen	13.9	14.0
oxygen	15.9	16.0
sodium	22.8	23.0
aluminium	26.8	27.0
phosphorus	30.7	31.0
chlorine	35.2	35.5
calcium	39.8	40.1
chromium	51.6	52.0

● What do you notice about the values for carbon, nitrogen, oxygen, sodium, aluminium, phosphorus and calcium on this scale (column 2)?

○ They are all slightly *less* (by 0.1–0.3) than whole numbers.

This can be changed by a slight modification of the scale. What column 2 shows is that:

$$\frac{\text{mass of hydrogen atom}}{\text{mass of oxygen atom}} = \frac{1.00}{15.9} \tag{10.1}$$

Now suppose that, instead of taking hydrogen as 1.00, we take oxygen as 16.0. Then from Equation 10.1, the relative atomic mass of hydrogen (the mass of hydrogen on this new scale) becomes $16.0 \times \frac{1.00}{15.9}$ or 1.01. Although both relative atomic masses are different on the new scale, their ratio $\frac{1.01}{16.0}$ is the same* as it was on the previous scale, $\frac{1.00}{15.9}$. Other relative atomic masses on this new scale are shown in column 3 of Table 10.1. Again, the ratio between any two of them is the same as it is for the column 2 values. To three significant figures, most of the values on this new O = 16.0 scale are whole numbers, although chlorine is a very obvious exception.

This was one reason why, for many years, scientists used a scale of this kind. In the rest of this block, we shall use the internationally approved relative atomic masses listed in Appendix 1 and also in the Study File for Block 6. We quote them to three significant figures. You can think of the scale as one on which oxygen takes the value 16.0. In fact the internationally approved scale is defined differently, and we allude to it briefly in Section 14.5, but the values are identical with the O = 16.0 scale even at the *four significant figure* level of accuracy.

On the O = 16.0 scale, at the four significant figure level, a surprisingly large number of relative atomic masses are close to whole numbers. This is both remarkable and important, but we defer discussion of it until Section 14.5. The relative atomic masses of those elements that occur naturally on the Earth, and can be obtained in weighable amounts, vary between 1.01 for hydrogen, which contains the lightest atoms, and 238 for uranium, which contains the heaviest. Some values are pictured in Figure 10.1a.

* If calculated, the two ratios are not exactly the same, but only because we are using relative atomic masses given to three significant figures.

Figure 10.1 (a) The relative masses of some atoms, and (b) the relative molecular masses of some molecules. In both cases, the data have been obtained from the relative atomic masses in Appendix 1.

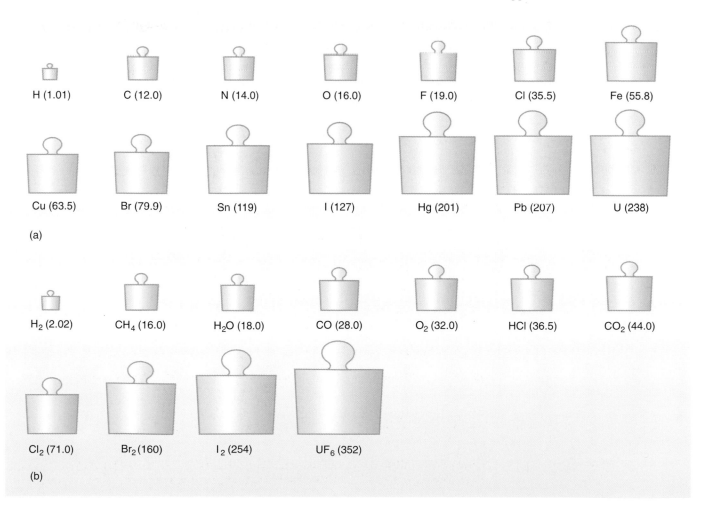

(a)

(b)

10.1 Relative molecular masses

Our scale of relative atomic masses can also be used to compare the masses of *molecules*. For example, the ammonia molecule, NH_3, contains one nitrogen atom and three hydrogen atoms. The nitrogen atom is about 14 times the mass of a hydrogen atom, so the ammonia molecule is about $[14 + (3 \times 1)]$ or 17 times the mass of the hydrogen atom. To be more precise, we use Appendix 1: the relative molecular mass of the ammonia molecule, NH_3 is $[(14.0 + (3 \times 1.01)]$ or 17.0. To obtain the **relative molecular mass**, all we need to do is to add up the relative atomic masses of the atoms in the chemical formula of the molecule. Like relative atomic masses, relative molecular masses do not have a unit.

○ Use the data in Appendix 1 to obtain the relative molecular masses of the molecules of water and carbon dioxide.

○ The values are: for H_2O, $[(2 \times 1.01) + 16.0] = 18.0$, and for CO_2, $[12.0 + (2 \times 16.0)] = 44.0$, respectively.

The values for these and a few other molecules are shown in Figure 10.1b.

10.2 The concept of the mole

What you have just learnt about the masses of atoms can now be extended to the masses of both atoms and molecules: the ratio between any two relative atomic or relative molecular masses is equal to the ratio between the actual masses of the atoms or molecules. For example, from Figure 10.1, the ratio between the masses of the chlorine atom and the carbon dioxide molecule must be $35.5 : 44.0$. This conclusion will now lead us to a most important concept.

Consider oxygen and hydrogen gases. They consist of the diatomic molecules, O_2 and H_2. The relative atomic masses of oxygen and hydrogen are 16.0 and 1.01, respectively.

○ So what are the relative molecular masses of the O_2 and H_2 molecules?

○ As Figure 10.1b shows, they are $(2 \times 16.0) = 32.0$ and $(2 \times 1.01) = 2.02$, respectively.

So this tells us that the masses of the oxygen and hydrogen molecules stand in the ratio $32.0 : 2.02$.

○ Suppose we take *ten* oxygen molecules and *ten* hydrogen molecules. What will be the ratio between their masses?

○ $32.0 : 2.02$; because the two masses contain the *same number* of molecules, they will be in the same ratio as the masses of the individual molecules.

So any two masses of oxygen and hydrogen that contain the same number of molecules will stand in the ratio $32.0 : 2.02$. This will be so whether the 'same number' is one, two, ten, or seventy-nine billion. Now let us reverse this argument. Oxygen gas consists of O_2 molecules and hydrogen gas consists of H_2 molecules. Suppose we weigh out 32.0 g of oxygen and 2.02 g of hydrogen.

○ What is the ratio between their masses and what does this tell you about the number of molecules in the two masses?

The ratio is 32.0 g : 2.02 g or 32.0 : 2.02. This is the ratio that signifies that the masses contain equal numbers of molecules. So 32.0 g of oxygen and 2.02 g of hydrogen contain the same number of molecules.

Let's go through it again. Oxygen gas contains just O_2 molecules, so if we weigh out 32.0 g of oxygen gas, we have 32.0 g of O_2 molecules. Likewise, 2.02 g of hydrogen gas contains 2.02 g of H_2 molecules. 32.0 g of oxygen and 2.02 g of hydrogen are the relative molecular masses of the two substances, followed by the symbol for the gram. These amounts are known as one *mole* of O_2 molecules and one *mole* of H_2 molecules, respectively. They both contain the *same number* of molecules.

Before moving to other substances, there are two matters worth raising. First, one mole of O_2 molecules and one mole of H_2 molecules contain the same number of molecules. But just what is this important number? It will obviously be very large because moles come in grams, and molecules are very, very small. Later, in Section 14.6, you will see how it can be determined. For the moment, however, we shall just call it *one zillion*. By avoiding some unpleasant arithmetic, this device should help you to get a clearer understanding of the meaning and usefulness of the mole.

Secondly, notice that a mole of a chemical substance is always coupled to a chemical formula. For instance, 2.02 g of hydrogen is one mole of H_2 molecules, so in this case, the chemical formula is simply H_2. This is such an important point that we shall give a special name to the chemical formula that we use when we calculate the mass of one mole of a chemical substance. We shall call it the **formula unit** of the substance. Thus the formula unit for one mole of oxygen molecules is O_2.

Oxygen and hydrogen are elements, but the mole concept is easily extended to compounds. Consider carbon monoxide; it contains molecules with the formula CO. Here, the formula unit is CO. We add up the relative atomic masses in the formula unit to get the relative molecular mass, and follow this with the symbol for the gram. This gives us (12.0 + 16.0) g or 28.0 g. One mole of carbon monoxide (CO) has a mass of 28.0 g.

What do 28.0 g of carbon monoxide, 2.02 g of hydrogen and 32.0 g of oxygen have in common?

They are the masses of one mole of the gases, because the relative molecular masses of the molecules CO, H_2 and O_2, as Figure 10.1b shows, are 28.0, 2.02 and 32.0, respectively. So the three masses contain the *same number* of molecules, a number that we have provisionally called one zillion. There are one zillion CO molecules in 28.0 g of carbon monoxide, one zillion H_2 molecules in 2.02 g of hydrogen and one zillion O_2 molecules in 32.0 g of oxygen.

Now let us generalize. The mole is an *amount* of a chemical substance. A chemical substance is one to which we give a chemical formula that, for the purpose of mole calculations, we call a formula unit. Moles can be looked at in two ways: either as an amount of the substance, or as one zillion formula units. Thus in the first place:

> one **mole** of a particular substance is the amount whose mass is obtained by adding up the relative atomic masses of the atoms in the formula unit, and following the number that is obtained by the symbol for the gram.

⬤ What are the masses of one mole of carbon atoms (C), one mole of methane molecules (CH_4), and one mole of carbon dioxide molecules (CO_2)?

○ 12.0 g, 16.0 g and 44.0 g, respectively; we add the relative atomic masses in the formula units. For methane this gives $[12.0 + (4 \times 1.01)]$ or 16.0; for CO_2, it gives $[12.0 + (2 \times 16.0)]$ or 44.0. We then follow these numbers by the symbol for the gram.

Secondly, a mole contains one zillion formula units. For carbon atoms, the formula unit is C; for methane molecules, it is CH_4; and for carbon dioxide molecules, it is CO_2. Thus, there are one zillion carbon atoms in 12.0 g of carbon, one zillion CH_4 molecules in 16.0 g of methane, and one zillion CO_2 molecules in 44.0 g of carbon dioxide.

Why are moles so important? First, the mass of one mole of a substance, which is called its **molar mass**, comes in grams, so it can be seen and weighed out. Secondly, they all contain one zillion formula units each of which comes as an atom, or combination of atoms. So moles connect the visible world of the laboratory with the invisible world of the atom and the molecule.

We end this section by reminding you that moles always have a chemical formula associated with them. We can reinforce this by using oxygen as an example. We have seen that one mole of oxygen molecules (O_2) has a mass of 32.0 g, and that this is what we get when we weigh out 32.0 g of oxygen gas. This mass contains one zillion O_2 molecules. But there is another way of looking at this 32.0 g of oxygen. Each oxygen molecule in it consists of *two* oxygen atoms, so in 32.0 g of oxygen gas, there will be *two* zillion oxygen atoms.

⬤ How many moles of oxygen atoms is this?

○ Each mole of oxygen atoms contains one zillion oxygen atoms so it must be two moles.

This is quite consistent with what you have already learnt about the mole. We are now dealing in oxygen *atoms*, and the relative atomic mass of oxygen is 16.0.

⬤ What is the mass of one mole of oxygen *atoms*?

○ The relative atomic mass followed by the symbol for the gram. This is 16.0 g.

So 32.0 g of oxygen can be thought of as one mole of O_2 molecules, or two moles of oxygen atoms. In the first case, we are using the formula unit O_2; in the second, the formula unit O. There is no contradiction provided we recognize that we are using a different formula unit in each case (Figure 10.2).

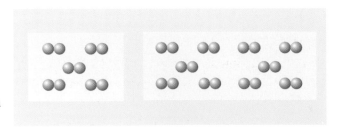

Figure 10.2 Here, for the purposes of illustration, one zillion is pictured as ten. In oxygen gas, which contains diatomic molecules, one mole of oxygen *atoms* (O) (left), has only half the number of atoms, and therefore only half the mass of one mole of oxygen *molecules* (O_2) (right). But both contain the same number of formula units: on the left there are ten O atoms; on the right there are ten O_2 molecules. The phrase *one mole of oxygen* is ambiguous; it needs a formula unit to make it precise.

Chemists prefer to use O_2 rather than O for the chemical formula of oxygen gas because it carries more information: it tells us that the oxygen atoms are grouped in pairs. But as we have seen, either formula can be used in the calculation of the mass

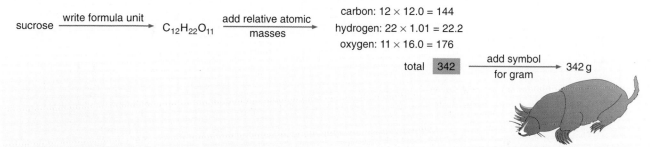

One mole of salt, NaCl, has a mass of 58.5 g. It contains one zillion sodium atoms and one zilllon chlorine atoms. There are about 8.5 moles in a half kilogram bag of household salt.

One mole of sucrose, $C_{12}H_{22}O_{11}$, has a mass of 342 g. It contains 12 zillion carbon atoms, 22 zillion hydrogen atoms and 11 zillion oxygen atoms. There are about 1.5 moles in a half-kilogram bag of household sugar.

of a mole of oxygen. It is because of cases like this that we have introduced the extra term, formula unit, for chemical formulae that are used in molar calculations.

Some of the important operations and ideas that were introduced in this section are summarized in Figure 10.3, where the mole concept is applied to two common household substances. These are salt (sodium chloride, NaCl) and sugar (sucrose, $C_{12}H_{22}O_{11}$).

Figure 10.3 How to work out the masses of one mole of table salt (sodium chloride, NaCl) and one mole of cane sugar (sucrose, $C_{12}H_{22}O_{11}$). One zillion is the, for the moment, unknown number of formula units which is present in one mole of all chemical substances.

10.3 Using moles to calculate amounts of reactants and products

A few calculations on chemical reactions will show how useful moles can be. To start with, the equation for the reaction is written down. *It must be a balanced one.* Let us use Equation 9.6 for the burning of methane:

$$CH_4(g) + 2O_2(g) \longrightarrow CO_2(g) + 2H_2O(g) \tag{9.6}$$

This tells us that when methane burns:

(a) Each molecule of methane (CH_4) reacts with two molecules of oxygen (O_2) to form one molecule of carbon dioxide (CO_2) and two molecules of water (H_2O).

It follows that:

(b) One zillion molecules of methane (CH_4) react with two zillion molecules of oxygen (O_2) to form one zillion molecules of carbon dioxide (CO_2) and two zillion molecules of water (H_2O).

⬤ How much methane contains one zillion CH_4 molecules, and how much oxygen contains two zillion O_2 molecules?

○ One mole or 16.0 g of methane (CH_4) and two moles or 64.0 g of oxygen (O_2).

Thus statement (b) can be rewritten as:

(c) One mole of methane (CH_4) reacts with two moles of oxygen (O_2) to form one mole of carbon dioxide (CO_2) and two moles of water (H_2O).

Statement (c) is the same as statement (a) except that the word mole has been substituted for the word molecule: moles react in the same proportions as the invisible molecules or formula units in the chemical equation. This is the first key point about moles; the second is that they are visible and weighable amounts. Using the molar masses implied by Figure 10.1b, statement (c) can be rewritten as:

(d) 16.0 g of methane react with 64.0 g of oxygen to form 44.0 g of carbon dioxide and 36.0 g of water.

Notice that because the equation that led to this conclusion was balanced, with the same numbers of each type of atom on each side of the equation, the law of conservation of mass is obeyed. The mass of methane and oxygen is equal to the mass of carbon dioxide and water (80.0 g).

When you turn on and light your gas rings, the air contains more than enough oxygen to supply the 64.0 g required by every 16.0 g of methane. We say that the oxygen is *present in excess*. However, each 16.0 g of methane that is burned will put 44.0 g of carbon dioxide into the atmosphere.

⬤ How much carbon dioxide does one tonne of methane put into the atmosphere?

○ If 16.0 g of methane yield 44.0 g of carbon dioxide, 1 g will yield $\frac{44.0}{16.0}$ g or 2.75 g. If 1 g of methane yields 2.75 g carbon dioxide, 1 tonne will yield 2.75 tonnes.

In the 1990s, the UK burnt about 43 million tonnes of methane (as natural gas) per year. The calculation that we have just completed shows that this put (43 million × 2.75) or 120 million tonnes of carbon dioxide into the atmosphere. It is interesting to compare this with human exhalation. A person breathes out about 1 kg of carbon dioxide per day or 370 kg per year. As 1 tonne = 1 000 kg, this is 0.37 tonnes per year. With a UK population of 60 million, human exhalation is 22 million tonnes per year, so UK combustion of natural gas produces over five times the carbon dioxide breathed out by the UK population.

This section has used moles to study a reaction in which carbon dioxide is a product. Now we apply them to a reaction in which it is a reactant.

10.4 Moles in space

People breathing in a confined space gradually increase the carbon dioxide concentration in the air around them. If this rises from its normal level of 0.036% by volume to above 6%, headaches and dizziness ensue. In spacecraft and spacesuits, this problem is tackled with chemicals that absorb carbon dioxide. One possibility is caustic soda or sodium hydroxide (Section 5). This has the formula NaOH. However, the metal lithium (symbol Li) also forms such a hydroxide with the very similar formula LiOH. Both of these solids absorb carbon dioxide, producing sodium carbonate, Na_2CO_3, and lithium carbonate, Li_2CO_3, respectively. The balanced chemical equations are:

$$CO_2(g) + 2NaOH(s) \longrightarrow Na_2CO_3(s) + H_2O(l) \qquad (10.2)$$

$$CO_2(g) + 2LiOH(s) \longrightarrow Li_2CO_3(s) + H_2O(l) \qquad (10.3)$$

In both these equations, one formula unit of CO_2 reacts with two of the metal hydroxide. As moles react in the same proportions as formula units, it must also be true that one mole of CO_2 reacts with two moles of the metal hydroxide. From Section 10.1 we know that one mole of CO_2 has a mass of 44.0 g.

⬤ Use Appendix 1 to work out the masses of two moles of NaOH and two moles of LiOH.

◯ Add up the relative atomic masses in the formula units. These are (23.0 + 16.0 + 1.01) or 40.0, and (6.94 + 16.0 + 1.01) or 23.95, respectively. Multiplication by two gives 80.0 g of NaOH, and 47.9 g of LiOH.

So 44.0 g of carbon dioxide can be absorbed by either 80.0 g of sodium hydroxide or 47.9 g of lithium hydroxide. But in a spaceship, equipment should be as light as possible.

⬤ On these grounds alone, would you choose sodium hydroxide or lithium hydroxide?

◯ Lithium hydroxide is better; it absorbs roughly its own mass of carbon dioxide. Sodium hydroxide absorbs only about half its mass.

Lithium hydroxide is the standard CO_2 absorber in US space programmes (Figure 10.4). Not only does it have a better CO_2 absorbing capacity, but reaction 10.3 also proceeds more quickly than reaction 10.2.

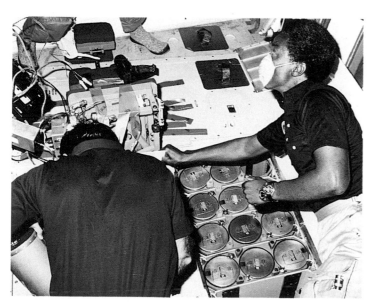

Figure 10.4   Replacing canisters of lithium hydroxide that absorbs carbon dioxide within the cabin and spacesuits during the missions of the US space-shuttle.

We have found that 44.0 g carbon dioxide react with 47.9 g lithium hydroxide, and you know from Section 10.3 that a crew-member will exhale about 1 kg of CO_2 per day.

What mass of lithium hydroxide is needed to absorb this 1 kg of carbon dioxide?

As 44.0 g of CO_2 react with 47.9 g of LiOH, 1 g of CO_2 reacts with $\frac{47.9}{44.0}$ or 1.09 g of LiOH. This means that 1 kg of CO_2 will react with 1.09 kg of LiOH. Thus about 1.1 kg of lithium hydroxide are needed per person per day of the missions.

10.5 Finding chemical formulae from chemical compositions

Now that we have a scale of relative atomic masses, we can use these to determine a chemical formula for any chemical substance from its chemical composition. This section sets out a formal way of doing this. Its examples are drawn from the chemistry of the so-called noble metals, platinum and gold (see Box 10.1, *Noble metals and royal water*).

Box 10.1 Noble metals and royal water

The metallic elements platinum and gold (Figures 10.5 and 10.6) are used in precious ornaments not just because they are rare and beautiful, but also because they are *noble* metals: that is, they combine reluctantly with other chemicals and, in particular, they are uncorroded by air and water. A corollary of this is that such compounds as they do form revert easily to the metals, for example on mild heating. In Section 10.5, such decompositions are used to establish the chemical formulae of a platinum chloride and a gold oxide.

One mark of the nobility of gold and platinum is that they are not attacked by any one of the three common concentrated acids of Section 2. But they will dissolve in a *mixture* of concentrated nitric and hydrochloric acids. Because gold dissolves in it, medieval alchemists gave this mixture of acids the Latin name of *aqua regia* ('royal water').

When James Franck, the Jewish scientist, left Nazi Germany for America in the 1930s, he entrusted his gold Nobel medal to a friend, the Danish physicist Niels Bohr. In 1943, during the Second World War, Bohr in his turn was threatened with Nazi internment. Before fleeing to England, he dissolved Franck's medal in *aqua regia*, and left the solution on a shelf in his Copenhagen laboratory. When Bohr returned to Denmark in 1945, the solution was still there. The gold was recovered and Franck's medal recast.

Figure 10.5 A platinum treasure trove: at the back, a terrace of platinum ingots, with rolled platinum bars in the foreground to left and right. On the watch glasses are coloured compounds and alloys of palladium, another noble metal, which resembles platinum.

Figure 10.6 A torc made from an alloy of gold, silver and copper, found near Snettisham, Norfolk, and believed to date from the 1st century BC.

You will be given the chemical composition of a compound, or some information from which that composition can be determined. For example, the metallic element platinum (symbol Pt) forms a solid red compound with chlorine. If a crucible containing this platinum chloride is heated to 400 °C, chlorine gas is given off, and platinum metal is left in the crucible. If, at the beginning, the crucible contains 3.75 g of platinum chloride, then at the end it contains 2.17 g of platinum. What is the chemical formula of the red compound?

The first step is to use this information to find what masses of the two elements are combined in the compound. Because 3.75 g of the chloride contain 2.17 g of platinum, it must also contain (3.75 − 2.17) g, or 1.58 g, of chlorine. Thus, in this chloride, 2.17 g of platinum are combined with 1.58 g of chlorine.

The second step is to use these combining masses to find what mass of one of the two elements combines with *one mole* of the atoms of the other. Let's find what mass of chlorine combines with one mole of platinum atoms:

2.17 g of platinum combine with 1.58 g of chlorine

so 1.00 g of platinum combines with $\dfrac{1.58}{2.17}$ g of chlorine

Now the relative atomic mass of platinum is 195; this means that 1.00 mole of platinum atoms has a mass of 195 g,

so 195 g of platinum combine with $\dfrac{1.58 \times 195}{2.17}$ g = 142 g of chlorine

that is, 1.00 mole of platinum atoms combines with 142 g of chlorine.

The third step is to find out how many *moles* of the chosen element (in this case chlorine) combine with one mole of the atoms of the other (in this case platinum). The relative atomic mass of chlorine is 35.5. Thus one mole of chlorine atoms has a mass of 35.5 g. Consequently, 142 g of chlorine contain $\frac{142}{35.5}$ moles, or 4.00 moles, of chlorine atoms. So, in the chloride,

1.00 mole of platinum atoms combines with 4.00 moles of chlorine atoms

The fourth step is to write down the chemical formula of the compound. This should be one that shows the atoms combined in the simplest possible ratio of whole numbers. We have found that one mole of platinum atoms combines with four moles of chlorine atoms.

Now you know that moles combine in the same proportions as atoms or molecules. It follows that, in the red chloride, each platinum atom is combined with four chlorine atoms. In this case, therefore, the simplest possible whole number ratio between the combined atoms is 1 : 4, and the required chemical formula is $PtCl_4$.

This last step can be a little more complicated. For example, gold (Au) forms an oxide that loses oxygen when it is heated. It is found that 3.50 g of the oxide lose 0.38 g of oxygen and leave 3.12 g of gold. If you carry through steps 1–3 of the type of calculation we have just performed, you will find that 1.00 mole of Au atoms is combined with 1.50 moles of O atoms.

Moles combine in the same *proportions* as atoms or molecules, but although it is quite all right to say that 1.00 mole of Au atoms combines with 1.50 moles of O atoms, we do not say that each atom of gold combines with one and a half atoms of oxygen because the atomic theory takes atoms to be indivisible. So we convert the ratio $1.00 : 1.50$ into the lowest whole-number equivalent, which is $2 : 3$. The formula of the oxide is therefore written Au_2O_3.

You will get the opportunity to try other calculations of this sort in Section 10.8, but it is important that you do at least one before moving to the next section. So try Question 10.1 now.

Question 10.1　In Section 7.7, we said that ammonia was 82.2% nitrogen and 17.8% hydrogen. Use this information to find the masses of nitrogen and hydrogen that are combined in the compound (step 1). Then find the mass of hydrogen that is combined with one mole of nitrogen atoms (step 2), and calculate how many moles of hydrogen atoms this mass amounts to (step 3). Finally (step 4), write down a chemical formula for ammonia, and check to see if it is the one given in Table 8.2. Take the relative atomic masses of hydrogen and nitrogen from Appendix 1. ◀

10.6 Empirical and molecular formulae

In Section 10.5, we established a formal method of calculating chemical formulae from chemical compositions and relative atomic masses. The formulae so obtained have an important limitation. This limitation can be demonstrated by repeating with ethane, a minor constituent of natural gas, the calculation that you have just performed for ammonia. Ethane's chemical composition can be determined by the method used for methane in Activity 6.1. The result (79.9% carbon and 20.1% hydrogen) was used in Tables 8.1 and 8.2.1.

This composition tells us that in ethane, 79.9 g of carbon are combined with 20.1 g of hydrogen. From this, 1.00 g of carbon is combined with 0.252 g of hydrogen, and 12.0 g of carbon (one mole of carbon atoms) are combined with 3.02 g of hydrogen. Now, 3.02 g of hydrogen are $\frac{3.02}{1.01}$ or 2.99 moles of hydrogen atoms. Thus, in ethane, one mole of carbon atoms (one zillion carbon atoms) is combined with three moles of hydrogen atoms (three zillion hydrogen atoms). It follows that each carbon atom is combined with three hydrogen atoms: the chemical formula is CH_3.

●　Is this the formula of ethane that you worked out in Activity 8.2?

○　No; there you found that ethane consists of molecules with the formula C_2H_6. Each ethane molecule is a collection of two carbon and six hydrogen atoms.

The chemical formulae that are obtained by the method of Section 10.5 are called **empirical formulae**. They tell us only the *ratio* in which the atoms are combined, and when empirical formulae are written down, that ratio is reduced to the lowest possible whole numbers. This contrasts with the **molecular formula**, which tells us the *actual numbers* of carbon and hydrogen atoms in each molecule of the gas. The empirical formula, CH_3, that we obtained for ethane is quite consistent with the molecular formula, C_2H_6, because in each ethane molecule, and therefore in the gas as a whole, the ratio of carbon to hydrogen atoms is $1 : 3$. However, the empirical formula CH_3 is also consistent with molecular formulae C_3H_9, C_4H_{12}, C_5H_{15} and so on.

Deciding which molecular formula is correct requires information that goes beyond chemical compositions alone. Cannizzaro found such information in the densities of gases, and his arguments lead to a straightforward way of deciding between the different molecular formulae. From Table 7.3, the densities of ethane and hydrogen at STP are 1.34 and 0.089 9 g litre^{-1}, respectively. Thus, at STP, 1 litre of ethane has a mass of 1.34 g, and 1 litre of hydrogen has a mass of 0.089 9 g.

⬤ What, according to Avogadro's hypothesis, do 1.34 g of ethane and 0.089 9 g of hydrogen have in common?

◯ Because they are the masses of the same volume of gas at the same temperature and pressure, they contain the same number of molecules.

Because 1.34 g of ethane and 0.089 9 g of hydrogen contain the same number of molecules, the ratio of the two masses, $\frac{1.34}{0.089\,9}$, must be equal to the ratio of the masses of the molecules themselves:

$$\frac{\text{mass of ethane molecule}}{\text{mass of hydrogen molecule}} = \frac{1.34}{0.089\,9} \tag{10.4}$$

Now the ratio between the masses of two molecules is equal to the ratio between their relative molecular masses. So we can rewrite this equation:

$$\frac{\text{relative molecular mass of ethane}}{\text{relative molecular mass of hydrogen}} = \frac{1.34}{0.089\,9} \tag{10.5}$$

⬤ What is the relative molecular mass of the hydrogen molecule in hydrogen gas to the nearest whole number?

◯ Two; the molecule is H_2, with a relative molecular mass of (1.01×2).

Thus, from Equation 10.5, the relative molecular mass of ethane is approximately $2 \times \frac{1.34}{0.089\,9}$ or 30.

⬤ The molecular formulae CH_3, C_2H_6 and C_3H_9 are all consistent with an empirical formula CH_3. What are their relative molecular masses to the nearest whole number?

15 = 12 + 3   *(12 = relative atomic mass of C)*
30 = (12×2) + 6
45 = 36 + 9

◯ 15, 30 and 45 respectively.

So only C_2H_6 has the correct relative molecular mass. This demonstrates the classical way of determining the chemical formula of a substance. The chemical composition is determined, and when this is combined with a scale of relative atomic masses, we obtain the *empirical* formula. This simply tells us the *ratio* in which the atoms are combined, that ratio being reduced to the lowest possible whole numbers. If the substance is a gas, or can be turned into one by heating, we can determine its density, and correct that density to STP. As the argument that led up to Equations 10.4 and 10.5 showed, Avogadro's hypothesis tells us that the ratio of the densities of two gases at STP is equal to the ratio of their relative molecular masses. So, comparing a gas with *hydrogen*:

$$\frac{\text{relative molecular mass of gas}}{\text{relative molecular mass of hydrogen}} = \frac{\text{density of gas at STP}}{\text{density of hydrogen at STP}} \tag{10.6}$$

But to two significant figures, the relative molecular mass of hydrogen is 2.0, so:

$$\text{relative molecular mass of gas} = \frac{2.0 \times (\text{density of gas at STP})}{\text{density of hydrogen at STP}} \tag{10.7}$$

Equation 10.7 allows us to select the *molecular* formula that is consistent with the empirical formula. The molecular formula tells us all that the empirical formula does: it gives the correct combining ratio of the atoms. But it also tells us the actual numbers of atoms in the tiny particles that move about together as a unit within the gaseous substance. The formulae that we use for gases in this block are all molecular formulae.

By contrast, the chemical formulae used for solids are usually empirical formulae. Thus CuO is the empirical formula of black copper oxide, and it simply tells us that the black solid contains equal numbers of copper and oxygen atoms.

10.7 A first look at valency

Up till now, we have concentrated on the *determination* of chemical formulae. But can these formulae be *explained*? What decides the ratios in which the atoms combine? The idea of valency is the first step towards an answer. In hydrogen chloride, HCl, each chlorine atom is combined with one hydrogen atom; in water, H_2O, each oxygen atom is combined with two hydrogen atoms. This number, the number of hydrogen atoms that one atom of an element combines with, is called the **valency** of the element in the compound in question.

○ What, then, are the valencies of nitrogen in ammonia, NH_3, and of carbon in methane, CH_4?

○ Three and four, respectively.

This definition of valency is equivalent to defining the valency of hydrogen as one. In HCl, where there are equal numbers of hydrogen and chlorine atoms, the valencies or combining powers of hydrogen and chlorine are equal. As hydrogen has valency one, chlorine has valency one also. In H_2O, the number of hydrogen atoms is twice the number of oxygen atoms, so oxygen has valency two. Notice that the assignment of valency one to hydrogen is corroborated by the fact that hydrogen gas consists of H_2 molecules: each hydrogen atom is combined with one (other) hydrogen atom and therefore has valency one. It begins to look as if valency might provide a way of connecting, or even predicting, the formulae of the compounds that an element might form. Let us look at an example.

Nitrogen with valency three forms ammonia, NH_3, with hydrogen which has valency one. But we have decided that chlorine also has valency one — the same combining power as hydrogen.

○ So what is the predicted formula of the compound that nitrogen forms with chlorine?

○ NCl_3, nitrogen trichloride; as hydrogen and chlorine have the same valency of one, each nitrogen atom will combine with either three hydrogen or three chlorine atoms.

This conclusion is correct. A chloride of nitrogen, NCl_3, is formed when chlorine gas reacts with a concentrated solution of ammonium chloride (Figure 10.7).

What do valencies imply about the formulae of the oxides of carbon? The valency of four for carbon is twice the value of two for oxygen: the combining power of carbon is twice that of oxygen, so each carbon atom will combine with *two* oxygen atoms and the formula of the oxide is CO_2. The valencies that we have assigned are

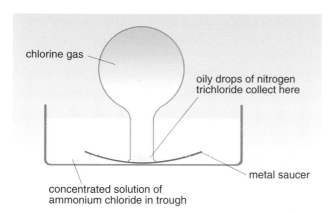

Figure 10.7 The valencies of nitrogen and chlorine suggest that nitrogen will form a trichloride, NCl_3. When a flask of chlorine is inverted with its mouth on a stout metal saucer standing in a concentrated solution of ammonium chloride, dense oily-yellow drops of this chloride collect in the saucer. The compound explodes most violently under the slightest shock.

therefore consistent with the formula of the most common oxide of carbon (carbon dioxide), but not with that of carbon monoxide, CO. In the latter compound, our rules imply that, as the carbon and oxygen atoms are present in equal numbers, the valency of carbon is *equal* to that of oxygen. This reveals something that limits the value of the idea: an element can have more than one valency. Nevertheless, if we can identify elements for which one valency is much more important than any other, then we can predict the formulae of many of the compounds that it will form. Table 10.2 shows the most important valencies of some common elements.

Table 10.2 The most important valencies of some common elements.

	Valency		
1	2	3	4
hydrogen (H)	oxygen (O)	nitrogen (N)	carbon (C)
lithium (Li)	magnesium (Mg)	aluminium (Al)	silicon (Si)
sodium (Na)	calcium (Ca)		tin (Sn)
potassium (K)	barium (Ba)		
fluorine (F)			
chlorine (Cl)			

These valencies can be used to predict the empirical formulae of binary compounds. You have already been through the carbon–oxygen example. But to turn this into a standard procedure, we must proceed a little more deliberately. Again, we start with the valencies of carbon (4) and oxygen (2). We now exchange the numbers against the elements. This gives us carbon (2) and oxygen (4). This tells us the combining ratio: every two carbon atoms combine with four oxygen atoms. To get the empirical formula, the ratio $2:4$ is converted into the lowest possible whole numbers; the result is $1:2$. So the predicted formula of the oxide of carbon is CO_2.

This gives us a formal procedure for the general case. Suppose two elements, A and B, combine to form a compound. Then if A has valency x and B has valency y, it follows that y atoms of A will combine with x atoms of B. The ratio $y:x$ can then be reduced to the lowest possible whole numbers to get the empirical formula of the compound.

If calcium is heated in nitrogen it forms a nitride. From Table 10.2, the valencies of calcium and nitrogen are two and three, respectively, so the principle just set down suggests that the empirical formula of calcium nitride is Ca_3N_2. This is correct.

The procedure works only if A expends *all* of its valency on B alone, and vice versa. When we ask you to apply it, you can assume that this is so. For example, the procedure works for methane, CH_4, but not for ethane, C_2H_6, which has the empirical formula CH_3. In ethane, only 75% of the carbon valency is expended on hydrogen; the rest is used on other carbon atoms. Such cases are discussed in   Block 8.

10.8 Summary of Sections 9 and 10

The essential points of Sections 9 and 10 are as follows.

1   We first compared the relative atomic masses of the elements by using a scale on which hydrogen was given a value of 1.00. If instead one adopts a scale on which oxygen has a value of 16.0, then the relative atomic masses of many elements are shifted closer to whole number values.

2   In this block, we use a scale of relative atomic masses, given to three significant figures, on which oxygen is assigned the value 16.0. Hydrogen, which has the lightest atom, then takes the value 1.01; uranium, which has the heaviest, takes the value 238.

3   The relative masses of molecules of substances on this scale can then be found by adding up the relative atomic masses of their constituent atoms.

4   The mole is an amount of a chemical substance. It always refers to a chemical formula that we call a formula unit. The mass of one mole can be obtained by adding up the relative atomic masses in the formula unit, and following the number so obtained by the symbol for the gram. This mass is called the molar mass.

5   Moles of different substances all contain the same number of formula units. This same number is large, and we have provisionally called it one zillion.

6   Because a mole always contains one zillion formula units, moles of the substances in a balanced chemical equation always react, or are produced, in the same proportions as the invisible atoms, molecules or formula units in the equation.

7   Consequently, molar masses can be used to calculate how much of a particular product in the equation might be obtained from a particular mass of a reactant, and vice versa.

8   A chemical formula for a substance can be obtained from its chemical composition by using relative atomic masses. One calculates how many moles of one element combine with one mole of another, and then reduces this ratio to the lowest possible whole numbers. This yields an *empirical formula*: it tells us only the ratio between the numbers of the different types of atoms combined in the substance.

9   If the substance is a gas, or can be easily converted into one, then a *molecular formula* can be obtained. This carries more information than the empirical formula. It contains the atoms in the ratio given by the empirical formula, but it also tells us the chemical formula of the tiny particles — the molecules — that move about as a single unit within the gas.

10 The molecular formula of a gas is obtained by determining its relative molecular mass. This can be found by doubling the ratio of its density at STP to the density of hydrogen under the same conditions (Equation 10.7). The molecular formula is then that multiple of the empirical formula that is consistent with this relative molecular mass.

11 The valency of an element is the number of hydrogen atoms with which one atom of that element combines. Elements may have more than one valency, but in many cases, one valency dictates the chemical formulae of many of the compounds that an element forms.

12 If element A has valency x and element B has valency y, then A and B are likely to form a compound in which y atoms of A are combined with x atoms of B.

In Questions 10.2–10.7, Sections 9 and 10 are broken down into the operations that you should be able to perform if you have understood the text. The operations are: equation balancing (Question 10.2, but see also Question 9.1); the calculation of relative molecular and molar masses (Questions 10.3 and 10.4); the calculation of the relative amounts of reactants and products (Question 10.5); the determination of empirical formulae from chemical compositions, and of molecular formulae from empirical formulae and gas densities (Question 10.6); the calculation of the empirical formulae of possible binary compounds from valencies, and of valencies from empirical formulae (Questions 10.6 and 10.7).

Section 10 brought out the full power of a long argument that began in Section 3, and was reviewed in Activities 6.3 and 7.1. Now Activities 10.1 and 10.2 continue the reviewing exercise. Activity 10.1 is a calculation, and you are strongly advised to do it. This is because it tests not just the listed operations from Sections 9 and 10, but also other important ones from Sections 3–8. It therefore assesses much of what you have learnt so far in Block 6. If you can do it, you have understood many important points.

Question 10.2 Hydrogen sulfide, H_2S, and sulfur dioxide, SO_2, are two colourless, poisonous gases. The former smells of rotten eggs; the latter has a pungent, choking smell. The two gases react together to form liquid water, and solid yellow sulfur, which can be swallowed (in moderate amounts) without harm. Write a balanced equation for the reaction; remember to include the states of the reactants and products. ◀

Question 10.3 What are the masses, in grams, of the following amounts of substances (to three significant figures): (a) one mole of nitrogen atoms, N; (b) 0.5 mole of nitrogen molecules, N_2; (c) 0.75 mole of oxygen molecules, O_2; (d) 2 moles of solid sodium chloride, NaCl; (e) 3.5 moles of propane, C_3H_8. ◀

Question 10.4 Which has the greater mass: a molecule of ammonia, NH_3, or a molecule of hydrogen chloride, HCl? ◀

Question 10.5 In Section 2, we described the ancient and inconvenient process for obtaining sulfuric acid that begins by weathering pyrite. Modern industry makes sulfuric acid from water, oxygen and sulfur. The process is carried out in stages, but the equation for the *overall* chemical change is:

$$2S(s) + 3O_2(g) + 2H_2O(l) \longrightarrow 2H_2SO_4(l)$$

A typical modern factory makes 2 500 tonnes of sulfuric acid a day. Calculate how much sulfur such a factory will consume each day. ◀

Question 10.6 (a) Aluminium metal and dark-red liquid bromine react together violently to produce white, solid aluminium bromide. Analysis shows that the chemical composition of this solid is 10.1% aluminium and 89.9% bromine. Calculate the empirical formula of the solid.

(b) Bromine forms a gaseous hydride, HBr. What, according to your formula, is the valency of aluminium in aluminium bromide?

(c) When aluminium bromide is heated it melts, then boils, and at 300 °C is a gas. The density of the vapour, when corrected to STP, is 23.9 g litre^{-1}. What is the molecular formula of the compound in the gas phase? ◄

Question 10.7 If the valency of aluminium is three (Question 10.6), use Table 10.2 to find the empirical formulae of the following compounds: (a) aluminium hydride; (b) aluminium oxide; (c) aluminium chloride; (d) aluminium nitride. ◄

Activity 10.1 Finding the molecular formula of arsine

In this activity, which can be done in parallel with the reviewing exercise of Activity 10.2, you will determine the formula of a hydride of arsenic that has revealed arsenical poisoning during many famous murder trials. The incentive to use it for this purpose was provided by a notorious case in which a guilty man went free (Figure 10.8). ◄

Activity 10.2 Reviewing important ideas from Sections 3–10

This activity reviews the argument of Sections 3–10. Taken together, Activities 10.1 and 10.2 revise much of what you should so far have learnt from Block 6. ◄

Figure 10.8 Bodle's farm, Plumstead, where the dirty deed was done: 'Along that self-same road, a young man strode at early morn on Saturday, November 2nd, 1833 — a young man fair of face and pleasant of tongue, with murderous villainy in his heart. He gave a gay "good morrow" to the gardeners and farm servants as they passed to their toil, but his thoughts were thoughts of avarice and murder, and deadly poison was in his pocket.' W.T. Vincent, *Records of the Woolwich District*, 1888–1890.

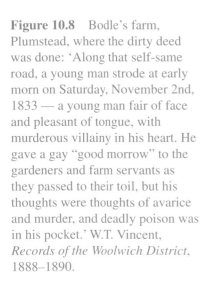

A second look at acids

11

In Section 2, acids were defined *operationally* by specifying their common chemical reactions. Thus, they dissolve in water and their solutions turn blue litmus red, they react with magnesium or zinc with liberation of hydrogen, and they react with calcium carbonate to give carbon dioxide. Then, in Table 8.2, we listed chemical formulae for our three common acids: hydrochloric acid is HCl, sulfuric acid is H_2SO_4 and nitric acid is HNO_3. What light do these formulae throw on the properties of acids?

○ What chemical element do all three formulae contain?

○ Hydrogen.

This hydrogen is the hydrogen that is displaced as a gas when the acids react with magnesium or zinc. The equations for the reaction of magnesium with sulfuric and hydrochloric acids are:

$$Mg(s) + H_2SO_4(aq) \longrightarrow MgSO_4(aq) + H_2(g) \qquad (11.1)$$

$$Mg(s) + 2HCl(aq) \longrightarrow MgCl_2(aq) + H_2(g) \qquad (11.2)$$

In these reactions, we have introduced the new state symbol 'aq'. This is shorthand for the word 'aqueous'. Its presence in brackets after a chemical formula indicates that that substance is dissolved in water: in **aqueous solution**. Notice, however, that water molecules, H_2O, do not appear in either equation. In these two cases, water is only the medium in which the reactions take place. The water molecules are largely spectators; no water is broken down or created during the reactions.

In Equations 11.1 and 11.2, the hydrogen atoms in the formulae of the acids are replaced by an atom of the metal, magnesium. We begin, for example, with a solution of sulfuric acid, H_2SO_4, and end with a solution of magnesium sulfate, $MgSO_4$. The sulfate group, SO_4, starts out on the left of Equation 11.1 combined with hydrogen; it ends up on the right, combined with magnesium. At the molecular level then, an acid is a substance containing hydrogen atoms that can be replaced in a chemical reaction by metal atoms, such as magnesium or zinc. Later, in Section 13.4, we shall see how this definition can be further refined.

11.1 Salts

After reaction 11.1 is over, you end up with water in which the substance magnesium sulfate, $MgSO_4$, is dissolved. If this water is evaporated by heating, the dissolved magnesium sulfate is obtained as a white crystalline solid. Likewise, evaporation of water after reaction 11.2 is over, leaves white crystalline magnesium chloride, $MgCl_2$. Substances such as magnesium sulfate and magnesium chloride are known as salts. **Salts** are formed when the hydrogen atoms of an acid are replaced by metal atoms. The name is taken from common salt, sodium chloride, which is the best-known member of the class.

○ What acid has its hydrogen replaced when common salt is formed, and what metal does the replacing?

○ Hydrochloric acid, HCl, has its hydrogen atoms replaced by atoms of the metal sodium, when sodium chloride, NaCl, is formed.

11.2 Basic hydroxides and alkaline solutions

Acids react in an important way with basic hydroxides. Basic hydroxides are solids that are members of a more general class of compounds called bases. You have already met some: they include sodium hydroxide or caustic soda, NaOH, and lithium hydroxide, LiOH. To these we can add potassium hydroxide, KOH, and calcium hydroxide, $Ca(OH)_2$, a white solid made by adding water to quicklime, CaO:

$$CaO(s) + H_2O(l) \longrightarrow Ca(OH)_2(s) \tag{11.3}$$

The dry quicklime gets very hot as its 'thirst' is 'slaked' by the water; calcium hydroxide is therefore sometimes called *slaked lime*. Notice the brackets in the chemical formula of calcium hydroxide. The formula contains two OH or hydroxide groups of the kind in Table 6.1. This is signalled by putting the OH in brackets that are followed by a subscript 2. The 2 signifies that the part of the formula that is inside the bracket should be doubled. So one $Ca(OH)_2$ unit contains one calcium, two oxygen and two hydrogen atoms. It is spoken 'see-ay, oh-aitch twice'.

○ What do the chemical formulae of the basic hydroxides have in common?

○ One or more hydroxide groups, OH, allied to a metal atom.

Whereas solutions of acids turn blue litmus red, aqueous solutions of basic hydroxides turn red litmus blue. Such solutions are said to be **alkaline**. Concentrated alkaline solutions are corrosive in their own distinctive way. They taste bitter,* have a soapy feel, and destroy hair and fat. This is why sodium hydroxide, NaOH, is marketed for the unblocking of drains. When the solution is hot, the corrosive power is increased. A chilling report survives from a 16th century Viennese soapworks where caustic soda was in use: 'a drunken worker, wearing woollen clothes, fell into the boiling liquid; he was consumed in an instant, and afterwards nothing was found save his linen shirt and the harder bones'.

11.3 Neutralization

In their different ways, concentrated acids and concentrated alkalis are very corrosive (Box 11.1, *Acids and alkalis: the murderer's friends?*). Yet those corrosive powers undergo mutual destruction when one type of solution is added to the other. Suppose litmus is added to sodium hydroxide solution; the solution turns blue. Now we add hydrochloric acid, little by little. To begin with, the litmus turns red where the acid is dropped in, but the solution again becomes blue if it is swirled. Eventually, however, if just the right amount of acid is added, the litmus is no longer blue, but purple, and at this point, if one more drop of acid were used, it would turn red. At this turning point, the solution tastes neither sour like an acid, nor bitter like a basic hydroxide: the corrosive properties of the acid and the basic hydroxide have both disappeared. Indeed, the solution has a nice salty flavour, and if it is heated one finds out why. Water evaporates and white crystals of sodium chloride, common salt, remain.

The equation for the reaction is:

$$NaOH(aq) + HCl(aq) \longrightarrow NaCl(aq) + H_2O(l) \tag{11.4}$$

---

* For early chemists, such as Joseph Gay-Lussac (Figure 7.18), tasting chemicals was just part of the day's work. **Modern practice forbids it absolutely.**

The dissolved salt is formed by replacing hydrogen atoms in the acid by the metal atoms of the basic hydroxide. At the same time, the hydrogen atoms of the acid and the hydroxide group in the basic hydroxide, combine to form water. Like Equations 11.1 and 11.2, the reaction takes place in aqueous solution, but this time water is a product, and so H_2O appears in the equation. Notice that it is written as liquid water, $H_2O(l)$, and not $H_2O(aq)$. 'Aqueous water' is, effectively, just liquid water!

Reactions like Equation 11.4 are called **neutralization** reactions. They take the form:

$$\text{base} + \text{acid} \longrightarrow \text{salt} + \text{water} \tag{11.5}$$

A **base** is a general name for a substance that can neutralize an acid. In the cases that we are considering, the bases are basic hydroxides.

As a further example, consider the neutralization of nitric acid, HNO_3, by calcium hydroxide, $Ca(OH)_2$. To form the water of Equation 11.5, the two hydroxide groups of $Ca(OH)_2$ must combine with *two* hydrogen atoms. Since each HNO_3 contains only one hydrogen atom, each $Ca(OH)_2$ must react with *two* HNO_3:

$$Ca(OH)_2(aq) + 2HNO_3(aq) \longrightarrow Ca(NO_3)_2(aq) + 2H_2O(l) \tag{11.6}$$

○ What salt is formed in this reaction?

○ Calcium nitrate, $Ca(NO_3)_2$: the two hydrogen atoms of two HNO_3 units have been replaced by a calcium atom.

Like $Ca(OH)_2$, the formula of calcium nitrate contains brackets. One $Ca(NO_3)_2$ unit contains one calcium, two nitrogen and six oxygen atoms. It is spoken 'see-ay, en oh-three twice'.

In these neutralization reactions, salts arise from a combination of the metal atoms of basic hydroxides with groups combined with hydrogen in the acid. Figure 11.1 shows some of the many different salts that can be made in this way. But in all such neutralization reactions, hydrogen atoms from the acid combine with hydroxide groups from the basic hydroxide to form water.

Figure 11.1   Some salts formed by combining metal atoms with groups allied to hydrogen in acids. From the left: calcium chloride, $CaCl_2$; manganese dichloride, $MnCl_2$; cobalt sulfate, $CoSO_4$; potassium chromate, K_2CrO_4; nickel dinitrate, $Ni(NO_3)_2$; copper sulfate, $CuSO_4$; magnesium sulfate, $MgSO_4$. The salts $MnCl_2$, $CoSO_4$, $Ni(NO_3)_2$ and $CuSO_4$ retain, in addition to the quoted formulae, water molecules from the aqueous solutions in which they were made.

Box 11.1 Acids and alkalis: the murderer's friends?

Mrs Durand-Deacon no longer exists. She has disappeared completely and no trace of her can ever be found again. I have destroyed her with acid. You will find the sludge which remains at Leopold Road. Every trace has gone. How can you prove murder if there is no body?

With these words, John George Haigh (Figure 11.2) confided his supposed achievement to Inspector Albert Webb. But Haigh was wrong. In the sludge at Leopold Road, there were 13 kilograms of body fat, three gall stones, part of a left foot, 18 fragments of human bone and Mrs Durand-Deacon's acrylic resin dentures. Haigh was hanged at Wandsworth on August 6th, 1949.

Figure 11.2 John George Haigh (1909–1949) dropped the bodies of his murder victims into acid.

Complete disposal of a body by chemical means is not easy. Haigh used concentrated sulfuric acid. This breaks down the corpse by absorbing water (Section 2.1.1) and forms a sludge, but body fat resists its action. Since concentrated alkaline solutions dissolve fats, these are promising alternatives, but Section 11.2 suggests that some bone may resist even boiling solutions. This was the experience of Adolph Luetgert, a Chicago sausage-maker (Figure 11.3), who placed his wife's body in a steam vat of potassium hydroxide in 1897. The police found bones, teeth and two gold rings.

Figure 11.3 Adolph Luetgert, the Chicago sausage-maker, preferred alkali. This contemporary drawing shows him supervising the crushing of the potassium hydroxide by an employee.

In *The Ballad of Reading Gaol*, Oscar Wilde imprinted quicklime on the public mind:

> And all the while the burning lime
> Eats flesh and bone away,
> It eats the brittle bone by night
> And the soft flesh by day...

This was reinforced when, in 1910, Crippen put his wife's remains into quicklime. But this is useless. Shakespeare had the clearer vision. As the gravedigger tells Hamlet, 'Water is a sore decayer of your whoreson dead body.' Quicklime absorbs water (Equation 11.3), and remaining solid, forms no sludge. As research on dead pigeons has shown, by absorbing water, quicklime slows the *natural* process of decomposition and *preserves* the body.

Some apparently untried alternatives have special dangers for the user. Concentrated nitric acid would release clouds of poisonous brown nitrogen dioxide gas. If you have a corpse to dispose of, avoid chemistry and try some other method!

11.4 Summary of Section 11

The main points of Section 11 are as follows:

1   Acids are substances containing hydrogen atoms that can be replaced, in chemical reactions, by metal atoms such as zinc or magnesium. Salts are substances that result from this replacement.

2   Basic hydroxides are solids whose formulae consist of a metal atom allied with one or more hydroxide groups. Their solutions in water turn red litmus blue and are then said to be alkaline.

3   In neutralization reactions, the corrosive properties of acid and alkaline solutions suffer mutual destruction. The hydrogen atoms of the acid and the hydroxide groups of the basic hydroxide combine to form water. When water evaporates, what remains is the solid salt formed by replacement of the hydrogen atoms of the acid by the metal atoms of the basic hydroxide.

Notice how the groups that were introduced in Section 6.3 have cropped up frequently in this section in the formulae and names of acids, basic hydroxides and salts. In particular, nitrate and sulfate groups were part of the formulae of both acids and salts, and indeed, sulfuric and nitric acids might equally be called dihydrogen sulfate and hydrogen nitrate, respectively.

Question 11.1   Perchloric acid, $HClO_4$, is slowly added to solutions of rubidium hydroxide, RbOH, and barium hydroxide, $Ba(OH)_2$.

(a) Write balanced equations for the neutralization reactions that occur.

(b) What are the names of the salts that are left when the solutions that are formed are evaporated to dryness, and how many atoms of the different elements are present in their formula units? ◀

12 Chemical periodicity

In Section 8.2, we mentioned that one of the attendees of the Karlsruhe conference was a scruffy-looking Russian called Mendeléev. His photograph appears in Figure 12.1; as you can see, we did not exaggerate. We also said that the argument that Cannizzaro laid before the conference was one of the most influential in the whole of science. A major reason for this was the influence that it had on Mendeléev. Many years afterwards, Mendeléev recalled what kindled the flame of the greatest idea that he was to have in a long and full life, the idea of chemical periodicity or, as he always called it, the Periodic Law:

> The decisive moment in my development of the theory of the Periodic Law was in 1860, at the conference of chemists at Karlsruhe, in which I took part, and at which I heard the ideas of the Italian chemist Cannizzaro. I noted immediately that the modifications that he proposed to the atomic weights introduced a new pattern, and it was then that I was struck with the essential idea of a possible periodicity in the properties of the elements on increase of the atomic weight.
>
> So I began to look about and write down the elements with their atomic weights and typical properties, analogous elements, and like atomic weights on separate cards, and this soon convinced me that the properties of the elements are in periodic dependence on their atomic weights. And although I have had my doubts about some obscure points, yet I have never once doubted the universal validity of this law, because it could not possibly be the result of chance.

Mendeléev's discovery started with the recognition that some chemical elements are much more alike than others. You can think of these groups of similar elements as chemical families. We begin with two families that are immensely useful in developing the idea of chemical periodicity.

12.1 The noble gases

As you know from Block 2, air contains nitrogen, oxygen, a little carbon dioxide, and some water vapour. If that was all, then pure nitrogen could be made by passing air first through a drying agent such as calcium chloride, then through soda lime to remove carbon dioxide, and finally over heated copper to remove oxygen. In 1894, an English physicist, Lord Rayleigh (Figure 12.2), made nitrogen in this way and found its density at STP to be $1.257\,2$ g litre^{-1}. When, however, he made nitrogen by passing ammonia over hot copper oxide (Section 7.7), its density at STP was $1.250\,5$ g litre^{-1}.

How could this discrepancy be explained? A Scottish chemist, William Ramsay (Figure 12.3), believed that the nitrogen that Rayleigh had made from air contained an impurity — a previously undetected gas of higher density. So, Ramsay removed not just water, carbon dioxide and oxygen from air, but nitrogen as well (Figure 12.4). This left him with about 10 cm^3 of gas for every litre of air that he started with. At first, Ramsay thought that this gas was a new chemical element, which he named argon; later it was found to contain a whole *new family* of gaseous elements. In descending order of their abundance in air, they are argon (Ar), neon (Ne), krypton (Kr), helium (He), xenon (Xe) and radon (Rn). You met all the members of the family in the video 'The composition of the atmosphere' in Activity 6.6 of Block 2.

Figure 12.1 The hypnotic face of Dmitri Mendeléev (1834–1907) has been likened to that of Svengali or Rasputin. Such comparisons are encouraged by his insistence on having just one haircut a year. His fame rests mainly on his boldness in using his Periodic Law to predict the properties of undiscovered elements. After Lecoq de Boisbaudron had announced the discovery of the new element gallium in 1875, he got a letter from Mendeléev. It informed him that Mendeléev had already predicted the properties of gallium, and that his experimental measurement of the density of gallium metal looked to be in error. De Boisbaudron then redetermined the density of gallium and found that Mendeléev was right!

Figure 12.2 Lord Rayleigh (1842–1919) did most of his early research in the family manor house at Terling in Essex, a habit that perplexed the staff. A.C. Benson, who wrote the words of *Land of Hope and Glory*, recalled the gamekeeper remarking that 'his lordship spends most of his time in his lavatory'. Rayleigh explained why the sky is blue, married the sister of the Conservative prime minister, Arthur Balfour, and in 1904 won the Nobel Prize for Physics for his contribution to the discovery of argon.

Figure 12.3 William Ramsay (1852–1916) read classics at Glasgow University, but then frustrated parental expectations by becoming a chemist rather than a clergyman. In 1904, he won the Nobel Prize for Chemistry: 'Rayleigh gave numbers about which there could be no reasonable doubt. I asked him then if he minded my trying to solve the mystery. He thought that the cause of the discrepancy was a light gas in non-atmospheric nitrogen; I thought that the cause was a heavy gas in atmospheric nitrogen. He spent the summer in looking for the light gas; I spent July in hunting for the heavy one. And I have succeeded in isolating it!'

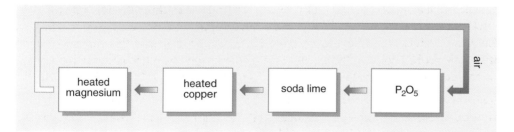

Figure 12.4 Ramsay's scheme for making argon. Air was continuously cycled over: (1) diphosphorus pentoxide (P_2O_5), a powerful drying agent, which removes water; (2) soda lime, which removes carbon dioxide (Section 5); (3) heated copper, which removes oxygen by forming CuO (Section 3.2); (4) heated magnesium, which removes nitrogen by forming magnesium nitride, Mg_3N_2. Continuous cycling was necessary because the reactions with copper and magnesium are slow, so prolonged contact is needed.

The properties of these elements are very remarkable. First, their molecules consist of *single atoms*. In this, they differ from the nitrogen and oxygen in air whose molecules contain pairs of atoms, N_2 and O_2. Secondly, they form very few chemical compounds. Indeed, helium, neon and argon form no compounds at all, even when heated with violently reactive elements such as fluorine and potassium. Although since the 1960s, some compounds of krypton, and especially xenon, have been made, the essential picture remains of elements with little or no inclination to combine with others. This separate existence, which sets them apart from other elements which are more chemically active, has given the family the name of the **noble gases**.

12.2 The alkali metals

The **alkali metal** elements include lithium, sodium, potassium, rubidium and caesium. What marks them out as a family can be seen on video in Activity 12.1. They are all soft metals that can be cut with a knife, and the surfaces, when so exposed, show the expected metallic lustre. In air, however, the shiny surfaces quickly become dull, because all of the metals react quickly with oxygen. The metals also react quickly, and in some cases explosively, with water (see title page) giving off a stream of hydrogen gas, and forming colourless alkaline solutions of the metal hydroxides, for example:

$$2K(s) + 2H_2O(l) \longrightarrow 2KOH(aq) + H_2(g) \qquad (12.1)$$

Another common family property is valency: in the many compounds that they form, the alkali metals always have a valency of one (Table 10.2). Thus, when heated in hydrogen, the metals form solid white hydrides, MH, where M represents the symbol for any of the alkali metals. On heating in chlorine, the metals yield solid white chlorides, MCl.

Activity 12.1   Chemical periodicity

In this CD-ROM activity, you will be introduced to chemical periodicity. You will then build up a table of the elements that embodies chemical periodicity — a table known as the Periodic Table. You should do the activity with Sections 12–12.2 still fresh in your mind. ◄

12.3 Summary of Section 12

The main points of Section 12 are as follows:

1   Some chemical elements are much more similar than others, so much so that they are grouped together in families and given collective names. Typical examples are the relatively unreactive noble gases (helium, neon, argon, krypton, xenon and radon) and the highly reactive alkali metals (lithium, sodium, potassium, rubidium and caesium).

2   If the chemical elements are laid out in order of relative atomic mass, similar elements appear at regular intervals. This phenomenon is called **chemical periodicity**, and is represented by Periodic Tables.

3   Figure 12.5 shows a **Periodic Table** for the first 20 elements. Chemical periodicity is marked by the appearance of similar elements in the same column. For example, the alkali metals appear in the column on the left; the noble gases in the column on the right.

						1 H	2 He
3 Li	4 Be	5 B	6 C	7 N	8 O	9 F	10 Ne
11 Na	12 Mg	13 Al	14 Si	15 P	16 S	17 Cl	18 Ar
19 K	20 Ca						

Figure 12.5   A Periodic Table for the first 20 elements. The order in which the elements appear is marked by a serial number above each symbol. Later (Section 14.3) this serial number becomes a quantity of even greater importance called the *atomic number*.

4   To produce such a neat chemical pattern, it is necessary to depart from the order of relative atomic masses at just one point. Figure 12.5 shows the serial number of each element in the table. Potassium is 19th and argon 18th, but the relative atomic mass of potassium (39.1) is less than that of argon (39.9). This suggests that there is only an *association* between the serial number of an element in the Periodic Table, and the order of relative atomic masses; there may be some more fundamental quantity that determines the order of them both.

5   Nevertheless, the order of relative atomic masses enables us to expand Figure 12.5 into a complete Periodic Table for all the known elements. By continuing to keep the alkali metals in a column on the left, and noble gases in a column on the right, we arrive at Figure 12.6 (p.115). Horizontal rows are called **periods**; vertical columns are called **groups**. The Table can be neatly divided up into blocks of elements (transition elements, lanthanides, actinides and typical elements) each with their own distinctive properties. The serial numbers run from 1–112, marking the fact that 112 chemical elements have so far been discovered.

6   In Activity 12.1, chemical periodicity was illustrated by putting together a mini Periodic Table from the **typical elements**, which occur at the extremes of Figure 12.6. This is shown in Figure 12.7. It consists of seven periods numbered 1 to 7, and eight groups numbered I to VII and 0.

7   Some of the important examples of chemical periodicity that are revealed by Figure 12.7 are as follows:

(a)   As the colour coding of Figure 12.7 shows, metals lie to the left, and non-metals to the right, with semi-metals in between.

(b)   When an element in Figure 12.7 forms one or more hydrides, then across the eight columns of the table, the valency of the element in the highest hydride (the hydride that contains most hydrogen) runs in the order 1, 2, 3, 4, 3, 2, 1, 0. Thus nitrogen occurs in the fifth column (Group V), so this hydride is NH_3 (ammonia). A very similar valency pattern occurs in the formulae of most highest chlorides.

(c)   In the fluorides and normal oxides* of the elements in Figure 12.7, the highest observed valencies are equal to the group number of the element. This allows the empirical formulae of the highest fluorides and highest normal oxides of the elements to be predicted. Thus, aluminium occurs in Group III, so the highest fluoride is AlF_3, and the highest normal oxide is Al_2O_3. These generalizations are not perfect. The oxide trend does not work for the elements H, Po, F, Br, I, Xe and Rn; the fluoride trend does not work for the elements H, N, O, Cl, Br, Kr, Xe and Rn. Nevertheless, both generalizations are true enough to be useful.

Section 12 now closes with just a single question in which you are asked to identify a chemical element from its chemical properties and approximate relative atomic mass. However, many other exercises of this sort are available in the question section of the CD–ROM for Block 6. You can assume that the trends summarized in point 7 above are perfect.

Question 12.1   A typical element Z from Figure 12.7 is a semi-metal and forms oxides with empirical formulae Z_2O_3 and Z_2O_5 and a single hydride, ZH_3. Its relative atomic mass lies between that of rubidium and xenon. Identify the element, and state the group and period of Figure 12.7 in which it lies. What is the formula of the highest fluoride of the element? ◀

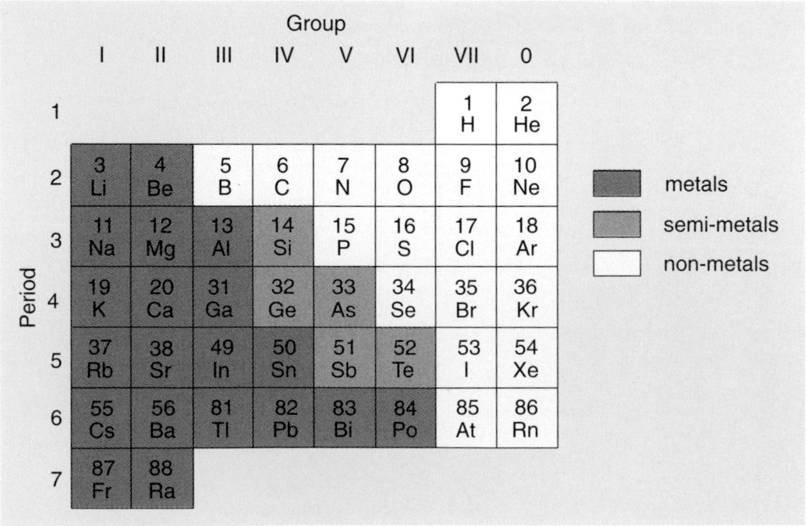

Figure 12.7   A mini Periodic Table for the 44 typical elements showing the distribution of metals, semi-metals and non-metals. The roman numerals across the top are group numbers; in most cases, they are equal to the highest observed valency of an element in that group.

*In normal oxides, *single oxygen atoms* are combined with the other atoms in the compound. This distinguishes them from peroxides and superoxides, in which the oxygen atoms are paired, as in the O_2 molecule.

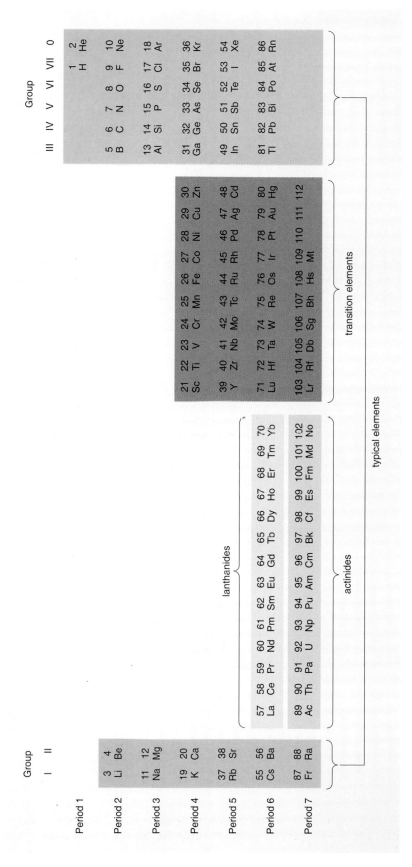

Figure 12.6   The complete Periodic Table for all of the known chemical elements. Metals occur to the left and non-metals to the right, with semi-metals in between. The named blocks of elements within the Table have their own distinctive properties.

13 Atoms and electrons

An important theme of the first half of S103 is *taking the world apart*, and you are now well down that road. You have met the tiny *atoms* of which the world is made; we have identified about 100 different kinds of atom, and we know their relative atomic masses. But outstanding problems remain. We do not, for example, know just how small atoms are, and we have no explanation of the extraordinary chemical periodicity that Mendeléev used to such astounding effect.

To make progress on both these problems, we need to confront an inadequacy in the atomic theory that has served us so well. Up till now, we have taken atoms to be the fundamental building blocks of matter, and, with John Dalton, regarded them as eternal and indivisible. But atoms are not indivisible; torch or watch batteries, for example, generate electric currents which, as you know from Block 5, are a flow of negatively charged particles called electrons. These electrons were once part of the atoms of chemical substances in the battery and its electrical circuit, and the currents appear when the electrons move from one sort of atom to another. So let's start our journey into the heart of the atom by reminding ourselves about electrons and electric charge.

13.1 A world of charge

In Block 5 Section 7, you met the concept of electric charge. Its unit is the coulomb (C). Electric charge is of two types, which we distinguish by the signs plus (positive) and minus (negative). Like charges repel one another; unlike charges attract. Charge is most familiar to us in the form of electric currents; these consist of a flow of negatively charged electrons. In Block 5, you learnt that each electron carries a negative charge of -1.6×10^{-19} C. Here, to simplify matters, we shall denote it $-e$. The opposite charge of $+1.6 \times 10^{-19}$ C will be denoted $+e$.

Figure 13.1 shows an experiment that generates static rather than flowing charges. A glass rod is rubbed vigorously with a piece of silk. Before the rubbing, both glass and silk carry no net charge (Figure 13.1a). Afterwards, both are brought up in turn to a third object, a positively charged rod suspended from a wire. The twist of the wire shows that the suspended rod is repelled by the glass rod (Figure 13.1c), but attracted by the silk (Figure 13.1d). That tells us that the silk has acquired an overall negative charge, and the glass an overall positive charge. The result is consistent with the **conservation of electric charge**. Like energy (Block 5), charge is conserved:

> In an isolated system, the total electric charge cannot change.

The total charge is calculated by adding the positive and negative charges in the way that we add positive and negative numbers. Before rubbing, both glass and silk had a charge of zero, so this was also the total charge. Afterwards, the negative charge on the silk, which we can call $-Q$, is equal to the positive charge, $+Q$, on the glass. When we add them, the total charge ($-Q + Q$) is zero, as it was before.

So far, we have said nothing about the atoms in the glass and the silk. However, as you saw in Block 5, atoms are neutral; they carry no overall charge, and this is why, to begin with, the glass and the silk in Figure 13.1 are neutral: they are made up from

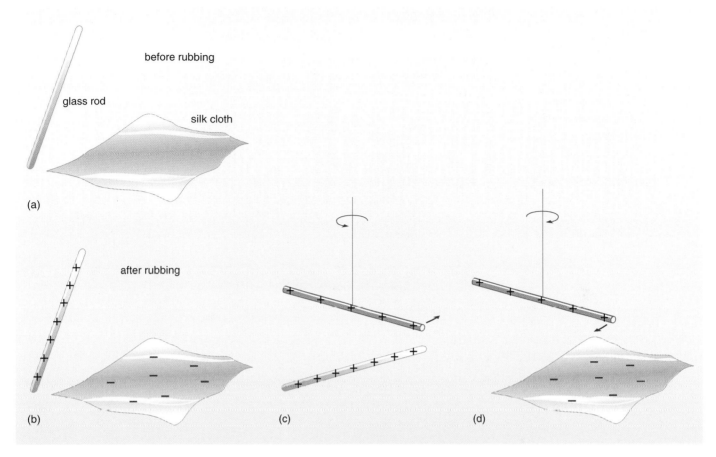

electrically neutral atoms. But we have argued that the easy generation of electric currents by electric batteries marks the fact that atoms contain electrons, each with a charge of $-e$.

○ How can this be so if atoms are neutral?

○ Charge conservation demands that the atoms must also contain positive charge, and the total amount of positive charge must be balanced by the total negative charge on the electrons.

Let's take two specific cases. A hydrogen atom, H, or a chlorine atom, Cl, is neutral: each contains equal amounts of positive and negative charge. If the hydrogen atom loses one negatively charged electron, the positive charge then exceeds the negative charge, and the hydrogen atom now carries an overall charge of $+e$.

○ Suppose the chlorine atom picks up one electron. What overall charge will it then have?

○ $-e$; the negative charge in the atom will then exceed the positive charge by the charge on the extra electron.

The hydrogen atom that has lost an electron and therefore has a charge of $+e$ is written H^+; the chlorine atom that has gained an electron and therefore has a charge of $-e$ is written Cl^-. Charged species such as this are called **ions**. Ions are often found in aqueous solutions.

Figure 13.1 The conservation of electric charge in glass and silk. (a) Rubbing an uncharged glass rod with uncharged silk leaves the silk with a charge of $-Q$, and the glass with a charge of $+Q$ (b), but the total charge remains zero as before. Note that this illustration shows equal numbers of positive and negative charges. The sign of the charges on glass and silk is established by the direction of the twist that they induce in a suspended positively charged rod (c and d).

13.2 Ions

In Figure 13.2, two conducting graphite rods have been connected by copper wires to the terminals of a domestic 9-volt battery. One of these wire connections also includes an electric light bulb. In Figure 13.2a the bulb remains unlit.

Figure 13.2 Graphite is the common form of carbon found in pencil leads, and is a good electrical conductor. In (a), the bulb remains unlit; in (b) it lights up.

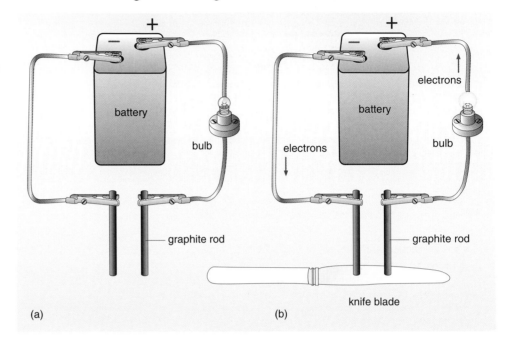

(a)   (b)

⬤ Why is this?

○ Because the electrical circuit is incomplete; there is an air gap between the conducting rods.

In Figure 13.2b, this omission has been rectified: an electrical conductor — in this case the metal blade of a knife — bridges the gap. Now the negative terminal of the battery can disgorge electrons, which pass anti-clockwise through the wires, the conducting rods, the bridging knife blade and the bulb on their way to the positive terminal of the battery. In Activity 12.1, you saw this flow of electrons ring an electric bell. Here it causes the bulb to light up. The illumination, then, is a test for the presence of an electrical conductor in the gap between the conducting rods. We can, therefore, find out if a *liquid* is a good electrical conductor by pouring the liquid into a pot, and sticking the two graphite rods into it.

If we do this with water or petrol, the bulb remains unlit: water is a poor electrical conductor, and petrol is even worse. But very different results are obtained if we use concentrated hydrochloric acid, a solution of HCl gas in water (Figure 13.3).

First, the bulb lights up, so electrons must be flowing round the circuit. Secondly, the dissolved HCl is decomposed into its elements. This process, in which a solution undergoes chemical change when it conducts an electric current, is called **electrolysis**. Water, laced with sulfuric acid, was decomposed by this method in Section 3.5. The conducting rods at which the circuit makes contact with the solution are called **electrodes**.

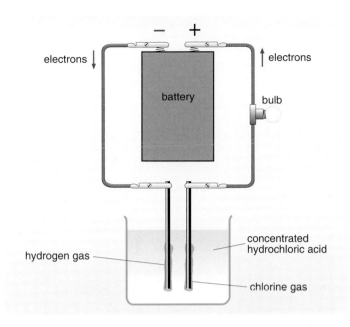

Figure 13.3 If the air gap in Figure 13.2a is bridged by a solution of concentrated hydrochloric acid, the bulb lights up, colourless hydrogen gas streams off the graphite rod wired to the negative terminal, and yellow-green chlorine gas streams off the rod wired to the positive terminal.

What has happened at the atomic level? Remember that unlike charges attract. The hydrogen particles in the dissolved HCl moved to the negative electrode.

- What does this suggest about those hydrogen particles?
- Since they move to the negative electrode, they are likely to be positively charged.

On the other hand, the chlorine particles went to the positive electrode.

- What does this suggest about them?
- They are likely to be negatively charged.

Now hydrogen chloride gas contains HCl molecules. But the electrolysis experiment suggests that the dissolved HCl in hydrochloric acid is in a very different condition: it consists of positively charged hydrogen particles and negatively charged chlorine particles. These particles are, in fact, the ions H^+ and Cl^-, which you met in Section 13.1. In hydrochloric acid, the dissolved HCl molecules, HCl(aq), have broken down into the *aqueous* ions H^+(aq) and Cl^-(aq):

$$HCl(aq) \longrightarrow H^+(aq) + Cl^-(aq) \tag{13.1}$$

H^+(aq) is called the hydrogen ion; Cl^-(aq) is called the chloride ion. The charge composition of these ions that we established in Section 13.1 allows an explanation of electrolysis (Figure 13.4). The positive hydrogen ions each have one electron fewer than a hydrogen atom. They move to the negative electrode where they meet the electrons flowing from the negative terminal of the battery. Imagine the arrival of two hydrogen ions. Each takes up one electron and forms a hydrogen atom, and the two atoms combine to form a molecule of H_2 gas. If we write each negatively charged electron as e^-, the superscript minus denoting its negative charge, then the process is:

$$2H^+(aq) + 2e^- \longrightarrow H_2(g) \tag{13.2}$$

Figure 13.4 Explaining what happens in Figure 13.3 using ions. Two hydrogen ions move to the negative electrode, take up two incoming electrons and form one H_2 molecule. Simultaneously, two chloride ions surrender two electrons at the positive electrode and form one Cl_2 molecule. Two electrons have thus been transferred across the gap between the graphite rods.

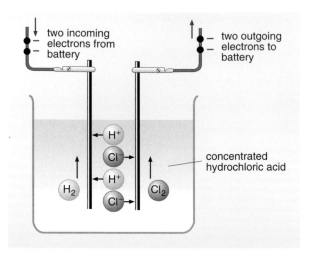

At the same time as this happens, we can imagine two negatively charged chloride ions arriving at the positive electrode. Each has one more electron than a chlorine atom. Each deposits that electron on the rod and a chlorine atom results. The two electrons then continue their journey to the positive terminal of the battery; the two chlorine atoms join together in a molecule of Cl_2 gas. This process is:

$$2Cl^-(aq) \longrightarrow Cl_2(g) + 2e^- \tag{13.3}$$

The net result of processes 13.2 and 13.3 is that two hydrogen ions and two chloride ions have been removed from the solution and converted into hydrogen and chlorine gas; at the same time, the movements and reactions of the ions have transferred two electrons across the gap between the electrodes.

13.3 Balanced equations containing ions

We wrote the breakdown of dissolved hydrogen chloride into aqueous ions as:

$$HCl(aq) \longrightarrow H^+(aq) + Cl^-(aq) \tag{13.1}$$

This equation is balanced with respect to its elements: there is one hydrogen and one chlorine on each side of the equation. But it is also balanced with respect to electric charge; that is, it obeys the law of conservation of charge. The hydrogen chloride molecules, and the water that they dissolved in, were electrically neutral: their total charge was zero. Consequently, the products of the breakdown of these molecules must carry an overall charge of zero. This can only be the case, in Equation 13.1, if the positive charge on the hydrogen ion is equal and opposite to the negative charge of the chloride ion.

Two other examples: like dissolved hydrogen chloride, dissolved salt and dissolved calcium chloride turn water into a good electrical conductor. So these two solids must also break down into ions when they dissolve in water. When sodium chloride, NaCl, dissolves, its chlorine particles assume the same form as those in hydrochloric acid: negatively charged $Cl^-(aq)$.

◯ So what form do the sodium particles assume?

◯ They become positively charged ions, $Na^+(aq)$, and so balance the negative charges on $Cl^-(aq)$.

This gives us a balanced equation for the dissolving of salt in water:

$$NaCl(s) \longrightarrow Na^+(aq) + Cl^-(aq) \qquad (13.4)$$

The total charge on each side is zero.

Now consider calcium chloride, $CaCl_2$. Each $CaCl_2$ unit that dissolves must yield *two* $Cl^-(aq)$ ions in the solution.

○ So what charge must be borne by the calcium in the solution?

○ There is only one calcium ion to balance the two negative charges on the two chloride ions, so its charge must be 2+; the calcium ion is written $Ca^{2+}(aq)$. Its charge is double that on a sodium ion because it has lost *two* electrons.

The equation for the dissolution of $CaCl_2$ is:

$$CaCl_2(s) \longrightarrow Ca^{2+}(aq) + 2Cl^-(aq) \qquad (13.5)$$

13.4 A final visit to acids and basic hydroxides

The three common acids that we first met in Section 2 are hydrochloric acid, HCl, nitric acid, HNO_3, and sulfuric acid, H_2SO_4. The aqueous solutions of all three conduct electricity: they contain ions.

○ What positively charged ion do you think that they all contain?

○ All three acids contain hydrogen, and in aqueous hydrochloric acid, this becomes $H^+(aq)$. So it is not surprising that $H^+(aq)$ is also present in aqueous nitric and sulfuric acids.

The equations for the breakdown of nitric and sulfuric acids in water are:

$$HNO_3(aq) \longrightarrow H^+(aq) + NO_3^-(aq) \qquad (13.6)$$

$$H_2SO_4(aq) \longrightarrow 2H^+(aq) + SO_4^{2-}(aq) \qquad (13.7)$$

Notice how these have been balanced. The single positive charge of the one hydrogen ion formed by the nitric acid formula, HNO_3, is matched by a negative charge placed on the nitrate *group*, NO_3, that is left when the hydrogen is removed. Here, the superscript negative charge that follows the NO_3 group shows that the *total* charge carried by the NO_3 group as a whole is $-e$. To emphasize the fact that the charge is carried by the *whole group*, some books put the group in square brackets and place the charge outside, e.g. $[NO_3]^-$. In this course, however, we keep things simple and omit the brackets. We have already noticed (Section 6.3) groups of atoms like nitrate (NO_3) that occur frequently in chemical formulae. Now we can see that they retain their identity in solution where they exist as charged ions. Thus, in our other example, the *two* positive charges on the *two* hydrogen ions formed by the formula H_2SO_4 are matched by *two* negative charges on the sulfate, SO_4. The resulting *nitrate and sulfate ions*, NO_3^- and SO_4^{2-}, contain more than one atom and are called **polyatomic ions**, to contrast them with **monatomic ions**, such as Na^+ and Cl^-, which are charged single atoms.

Another important polyatomic ion is the hydroxide ion, $OH^-(aq)$, which is present in aqueous solutions of basic hydroxides such as NaOH:

$$NaOH(s) \longrightarrow Na^+(aq) + OH^-(aq) \qquad (13.8)$$

All of the chemical groups that you first met in Table 6.1 may occur as polyatomic ions in aqueous solution. The last column of Table 13.1 lists these and other polyatomic ions, along with their names and correct charges. The table also shows some common positive and negative monatomic ions. Notice that metallic elements, such as the alkali metals and magnesium, form positive ions. The **halogens** (fluorine, chlorine, bromine and iodine) that you met in Activity 12.1 form negative ions.

Table 13.1 Some common aqueous ions.

Monatomic positive ions	Monatomic negative ions	Polyatomic ions
H^+	F^-	NH_4^+ (ammonium)
Li^+	Cl^-	OH^- (hydroxide)
Na^+	Br^-	NO_3^- (nitrate)
K^+	I^-	ClO_4^- (perchlorate)
Ag^+	S^{2-}	CO_3^{2-} (carbonate)
Mg^{2+}		SO_4^{2-} (sulfate)
Ca^{2+}		PO_4^{3-} (phosphate)
Cu^{2+}		HCO_3^- (hydrogen carbonate)
Al^{3+}		HSO_4^- (hydrogen sulfate)

Now let us return to acids.

⬤ What, according to Equations 13.1, 13.6 and 13.7, do aqueous solutions of hydrochloric, nitric and sulfuric acid have in common?

◯ They all contain aqueous hydrogen ions, $H^+(aq)$.

This is the final, chosen definition for an acid in this course: an **acid** is a substance that contains hydrogen and yields hydrogen ions when it dissolves in water. It is, for example, the presence of aqueous hydrogen ions in an acid solution that causes blue litmus to turn red. The fundamental role that hydrogen ions play in the properties of acids can be seen by looking again at the neutralization of acids by basic hydroxides; for example, Equation 11.4 of Section 11.3:

$$HCl(aq) + NaOH(aq) \longrightarrow NaCl(aq) + H_2O(l) \tag{13.9}$$

In Section 11.3, we noted that all such reactions had one thing in common: the combination of the hydrogen of the acid with the hydroxide group of the basic hydroxide to form water. But now we know that these groups are present as $H^+(aq)$ in the solution of the acid, and as $OH^-(aq)$ in the solution of the basic hydroxide.

⬤ So what happens when the two solutions are mixed and react together?

◯ The hydrogen and hydroxide ions combine to form water:

$$H^+(aq) + OH^-(aq) \longrightarrow H_2O(l) \tag{13.10}$$

As in Section 11.3, water is written $H_2O(l)$, not $H_2O(aq)$. Equation 13.10 is the fundamental neutralization process. It also suggests a new definition for a basic hydroxide: a **basic hydroxide** is a chemical compound whose formula contains one or more hydroxide groups, and which dissolves in water to yield aqueous hydroxide ions; for example:

$$Mg(OH)_2(s) \longrightarrow Mg^{2+}(aq) + 2OH^-(aq) \qquad (13.11)$$

It is the presence of $OH^-(aq)$ ions in an aqueous solution of a basic hydroxide that makes the solution alkaline and turns red litmus blue.

In Figure 7.17 and Activity 13.1, you see that a solution of ammonia, NH_3, in water is alkaline: it turns red litmus blue. Again, this is because hydroxide ions are formed, although the equation for the dissolution is less obvious than it is for a basic hydroxide:

$$NH_3(g) + H_2O(l) \longrightarrow NH_4^+(aq) + OH^-(aq) \qquad (13.12)$$

As you can see, ammonium ions are also produced. The ammonium ion is the only positively charged polyatomic ion in Table 13.1.

The definitions of an acid and a basic hydroxide given in this section are called the Arrhenius definitions, after Svante Arrhenius, who first proposed that acids, basic hydroxides and salts break down or *dissociate* into ions when dissolved in water.

Activity 13.1 Alkalis, acids and ions

In this activity you will watch the fourth and last video sequence for this block. It demonstrates experiments that we have already used in the text to introduce you to acids, alkalis and ions. ◀

Activity 2.2 A glossary of chemical substances (continued)

If you have been compiling a glossary of chemical substances this would be a good time to complete it. ◀

13.5 Summary of Section 13

The main points of Section 13 are as follows:

1 Atoms contain negatively charged electrons; each electron bears a charge of $-e$.

2 Electric charge is conserved: in an isolated system, the total charge cannot change. As neutral atoms contain electrons, they must also contain positive charge, and the total amount of positive charge must balance the total negative charge of their electrons.

3 Ions are charged particles that are formed when neutral atoms, or groups of atoms, gain or lose electrons. Loss of electrons gives positive ions; gain of electrons gives negative ions.

4 Water is a poor conductor of electricity, but when hydrogen chloride is dissolved in it, yielding hydrochloric acid, the conductivity is greatly increased. This is because the solution now contains aqueous ions.

5 During the conductivity test on hydrochloric acid, chemical changes occur at the electrodes: chlorine gas appears at the positive electrode and hydrogen gas at the negative one. Such chemical changes are called electrolysis. They happen because the aqueous ions move to an electrode of opposite charge.

6   When other acids, basic hydroxides and salts dissolve in water, they, too, increase its conductivity by forming ions. Some of these ions contain more than one atom.

7   The ions are formed by the breakdown of the dissolving substance when it enters the water. This breakdown can be described by a chemical equation, which is balanced with respect both to numbers of atoms and to charge.

8   Acids are substances containing hydrogen that yield hydrogen ions, H^+(aq), when they dissolve in water; basic hydroxides are substances that dissolve in water and yield hydroxide ions, OH^-(aq). In neutralization reactions, the hydrogen and hydroxide ions combine to form water.

Your understanding of these points is tested by Questions 13.1 and 13.2, which are concerned with the writing of balanced chemical equations for an electrolysis, and for the dissolving of substances that give ions in aqueous solution.

Finally, let's reflect on how this section has altered our developing view of the world. The atoms that we have spent so much time on are electrically neutral only because they contain equal numbers of positive and negative charges. Question 13.3 tests your understanding of this point. As well as a world of atoms, we now have a world of charge. We have detected the negative charge in atoms in the form of electrons. But somewhere in the atom, in some form or other, there must also be positively charged material, and we have not yet detected this directly. This is the thought that you should carry with you when you move on to Section 14.

Question 13.1   In Section 13, you met the ions H^+, Na^+, Cl^-, NO_3^- and SO_4^{2-}. When the following substances dissolve in water, one of these ions is a product. Use this fact to write a balanced equation for the dissolution, and to deduce the charge on the other ion that is formed: (a) sodium iodide, NaI(s); (b) perchloric acid, $HClO_4$(l); (c) magnesium sulfate, $MgSO_4$(s); (d) aluminium chloride, $AlCl_3$(s); (e) sodium phosphate, Na_3PO_4(s); (f) potassium sulfate, K_2SO_4(s); (g) ammonium nitrate, NH_4NO_3(s). When you have finished, check your deduced ions and charges against Table 13.1. ◀

Question 13.2   Copper chloride, $CuCl_2$, is a green solid that dissolves in water to give a conducting solution. If the solution is electrolysed, a red metallic film is deposited on the negative electrode, and a yellow-green gas is evolved from the positive electrode. Write an equation for the dissolution of $CuCl_2$ in water, and for the reactions that take place at each electrode. ◀

Question 13.3   What changes in the number of electrons are needed to convert (a) an aluminium atom, Al, into the ion Al^{3+}, and (b) an oxygen atom, O, into the ion O^{2-}? ◀

Activity 13.2   Practical work: iron, vinegar and electrolysis

It is possible to do experiments on metals and electrolysis at home. If you want to try this, look at the notes in your Study File. ◀

Taking the atom apart

14

At the end of the last section we suggested that atoms contained negatively charged electrons and a source of balancing positive charge. It is the electrons extracted from atoms that provide the current from our familiar electric batteries. But we gave you no direct evidence for the positively charged material; its presence was deduced only by default. Positively charged material from within the atoms is much more difficult to extract. As you will see, there is a reason for this: the electrons are in the outermost part of the atom, and the positive charges are on the inside. That this is so first became apparent from the study of radioactivity.

14.1 Radioactivity

You will have heard radioactivity mentioned in everyday speech. It was discovered in 1896, when the Frenchman, Henri Becquerel, wrapped up a uranium compound in the dark with a photographic plate. When he developed the plate, it looked as if it had suffered exposure to light. Evidently, uranium compounds emit 'rays' or radiation which, although invisible, resemble light in affecting photographic film. Such substances are said to display **radioactivity**.

The radiation from uranium compounds is of three different types. This can be demonstrated by passing it between the poles of a powerful U-shaped magnet (Figure 14.1). The stream of radiation is split into three smaller streams, which we label with the Greek letters alpha (α), beta (β) and gamma (γ).

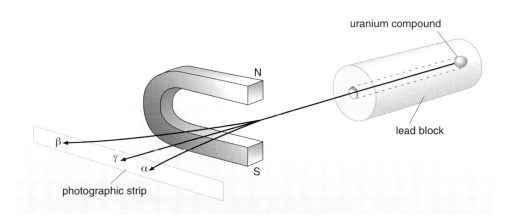

Figure 14.1 A schematic diagram of an experiment that shows that a uranium compound emits three kinds of radiation. The compound is placed in a horizontal shaft drilled in a block of lead. The radiation is stopped by lead, so it can emerge only along the line of the shaft in a horizontal direction. When it passes between the north and south poles of a powerful U-shaped magnet, it is divided into three streams labelled α, β and γ.

The γ-stream or γ-radiation is undeflected by the magnet and just goes straight on. This is what visible light would do, and indeed, γ-**rays** are just radiation at the short-wavelength end of the electromagnetic spectrum that you met in Section 5 of Block 2. They resemble X-rays.

By contrast, the α- and β-streams in Figure 14.1 are deflected by the magnet. This indicates that they consist not of electromagnetic radiation like light, but of *charged particles*: moving charged particles are deflected by a magnetic field. Moreover, the α- and β-streams are deflected in *opposite* directions. This shows that they have *opposite* charges.

You have already met one charged particle in this block. It is the electron, and its charge is negative. The β-**particles** in Figure 14.1 are fast-moving electrons, so they have a negative charge.

⬤ What charge do the α-particles carry?

⬤ Because they have an opposite charge to the electrons, they are positively charged.

The essence of a particle is that it has mass: α- and β-particles are evidence that radioactive atoms are, quite spontaneously, firing off bits of charged matter. The mass of an electron (a β-particle) is very small; it is only about one two-thousandth of the mass of a hydrogen atom. But the mass of the positively charged α-**particle** is much greater; it is about four times that of a hydrogen atom.

In the rest of this block, we shall largely ignore the β-particles and γ-rays, and concentrate on the α-particles. In Section 13.1 we wrote the charge, -1.6×10^{-19} C, as $-e$. The charge on an α-particle is found to be $+2e$. This is our first direct evidence of the elusive, positively charged part of the atom that we mentioned at the start of this section. But there is a problem. So far, uranium and its compounds have been our source of radioactivity, and the intensity of the α-particles and other radiation emanating from uranium is very weak. Can we find a more intense source of α-particles?

14.2 Radium

One morning in 1898, a heavy wagon drew up alongside a ramshackle shed in a Parisian courtyard and unloaded one tonne of dirt contained in sacks. A young woman appeared, opened one of the sacks, and ran her hands through the earth inside. It still contained the pine needles from its Bohemian home, 500 miles to the east. This was waste from the St Joachimstahl pitchblende mine. Pitchblende is an ore of uranium. In experiments at the nearby Ecole Municipal de Physique et Chemie, the young woman had used radiation detectors, similar to the familiar Geiger counter, to establish that it was four times as radioactive as uranium itself. She had decided that pitchblende must contain some unknown, but intensely radioactive element that remained in the waste residues after the uranium had been removed. With her husband, she intended to isolate it; they were the Curies, Pierre and Marie (Figure 14.2).

Figure 14.2 In this family the majority of Nobel Prize winners were women. Marie Sklodowska-Curie (1867–1934) who was Polish, shared her first prize with her French husband, Pierre, for their work in Paris on radioactivity. After Pierre's death in a road accident in 1906, she won a second prize in 1911 for isolating radium. Their daughter Irene (1897–1956) shared the 1935 Prize for Chemistry with her husband, Frederick Joliot. Both Marie and Irene died of acute leukaemia as a result of exposure to radioactive substances before the dangers were fully appreciated.

In some early experiments, the Curies found that when they extracted the element barium from small amounts of the mine waste, radiation detectors showed it to be intensely radioactive. This seemed extraordinary, because natural barium is not usually radioactive at all. Marie concluded that the radioactivity in the barium samples came from an *impurity*, the new radioactive element. Because this new element stuck with the barium in chemical reactions, it must be chemically very like barium. She and Pierre called it *radium*.

To obtain the new element, Marie now devised a method of extracting the barium in the mine waste as barium chloride. Kilogram by kilogram the Curies processed the waste in the yard in vats, with Marie, the chemist, stirring the brew with a long iron pole. Then the barium salts were taken into the shed, where the small amounts of radium chloride that they contained were separated from the barium chloride by repeated crystallization (see Section 2.2). Here Pierre, the physicist, made the radiation measurements. Night visits to the shed were a dramatic revelation of the Curies' progress. The increasingly pure radium chloride concentrates, scattered around the shed in dishes and on watch-glasses began to glow with a bluish light. Eventually, after 4 years, the Curies obtained about 0.2 g of radium chloride from the tonne of waste, an extraordinary feat of skill and tenacity.

Activity 14.1 Prediction using the Periodic Table

In this activity, you will use your understanding of the Periodic Table to deduce some of the properties of radium. ◀

14.2.1 The disintegration of radium

When a radium salt, such as radium chloride, is freshly crystallized from water, impurities with radioactivities of their own are eliminated. In this purified form, the radium salt then emits no β-particles; its emission consists of an intense stream of α-particles. Here then is the more intense source of α-particles that we were seeking at the end of Section 14.1. But what is left of the radium atoms when the α-particles have departed?

If the freshly crystallized salt is sealed up in a confined space, there accumulates around it a radioactive gas. Figure 14.3 shows an experiment that reveals that this gas is a mixture that contains both radioactive and non-radioactive components.

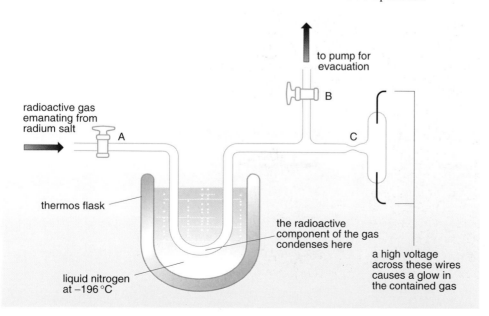

Figure 14.3 An experiment that separates the two gases that accumulate around a radium salt, such as radium chloride.

to pump for evacuation

B

radioactive gas emanating from radium salt

A

C

thermos flask

the radioactive component of the gas condenses here

a high voltage across these wires causes a glow in the contained gas

liquid nitrogen at –196 °C

To begin with, tap A is closed, and tap B is open, so the pump evacuates the space. Now B is closed and A is gently opened; the radioactive gas from around the radium salt then enters. All the radioactivity concentrates in the U-tube surrounded by liquid nitrogen: the gas contains a radioactive component, which is liquid at $-196\,°C$. But there is also a non-radioactive component, which is not condensed. This can be studied by melting the glass at constriction C, so sealing and drawing off the short vertical wired tube. If a high voltage is connected across the wires, the greenish-white colour characteristic of *helium* is seen. It is just this sort of process that is used to produce the familiar red glow of 'neon signs'; the difference is that the tubes in the sign contain not helium, but a different noble gas, neon.

When the container of liquid nitrogen is removed, the radioactive liquid in the U-tube warms up, boils, and turns into a very unreactive gas. This is the noble gas *radon*, which therefore appears in the same group as helium, argon and xenon in the Periodic Table (Figure 12.7). It also comes just two spaces before radium (Figure 14.4).

Figure 14.4 A fragment of the mini-Periodic Table of Figure 12.7. Radon (Rn), the radioactive gas generated by radium decay, is a noble gas from Group 0, and appears in position 86, two places before radium (position 88).

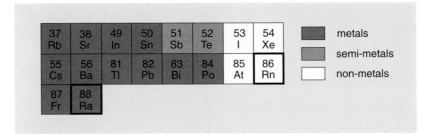

This experiment reveals the essence of radioactivity: *it involves a disintegration of atoms*. Such processes are known as **radioactive decay**. Radium atoms, it seems, can spontaneously tear themselves apart, and break down into radon and helium atoms. (*Some* of the helium detected in Figure 14.3 comes from the decay of radon itself (see Question 14.5).) The disintegration of the radium occurs regardless of the chemical compound in which it is to be found: it happens in radium metal, radium bromide, radium sulfate or any other radium compound (Box 14.1, *Mr Watras's radon problem*).

Box 14.1 *Mr Watras's radon problem*

It was not something that the managers of the Pennsylvanian nuclear power station were used to: dangerous levels of radiation creeping in from outside. It came in the wholly innocent shape of Stanley J. Watras, one of their employees. As he strolled through the gates on 19 December 1984, the radiation alarms began to ring. Eventually, they traced the problem to the levels of radon gas in his home. The maximum dose allowed by the nuclear industry over a five-year period could be picked up in Mr Watras's kitchen in just one week.

Radon in homes is formed from radium, which is formed in its turn from other radioactive elements, such as thorium and uranium, in the underlying rocks. Because radon is a gas, it can diffuse up into the houses above. There it decays into other radioactive

elements, such as polonium, that form solids. These attach themselves to airborne dust, so they can then be breathed in, and deposited in the lungs. Alternatively, radon that has been inhaled may decay within the lungs, and the polonium product can then attach itself directly to the lung walls. In either case, the radioactivity raises the risk of lung cancer.

In the UK, health regulations recommend action when radon levels in the home are more than 10 times the national average. Action may involve incorporation of an underfloor radon-proof barrier, and forced ventilation of the underfloor space. Figure 14.5 suggests that Cornwall, Devon, Derbyshire and Northamptonshire are places where it may be needed. Nevertheless, the UK action limit is still only one five-hundredth of that found in Mr Watras's kitchen!

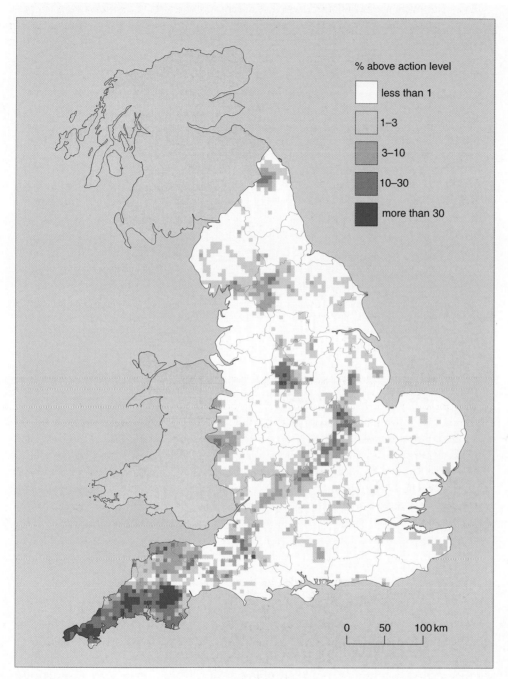

Figure 14.5 A map of England showing the percentages of homes with radon levels above the recommended action limit.

% above action level

less than 1

1–3

3–10

10–30

more than 30

0   50   100 km

The breakdown of radium into helium and radon also makes quantitative sense. In Appendix 1, the relative atomic masses of radium, radon and helium are listed as 226, 222 and 4.00, respectively.

○ Do these values suggest that the disintegration of a radium atom obeys the law of conservation of mass?

○ Yes; the sum of the relative atomic masses of the products of the disintegration, radon and helium, is (222 + 4.00) or 226. This is equal to the relative atomic mass of radium.

Now let's think about the α-particle that is emitted when the radium atom disintegrates. In Section 14.1, you were told that α-particles have a mass four times that of a hydrogen atom.

⬤ Of which product of the disintegration of a radium atom is this also true?

◯ Of the helium atom: this has a relative atomic mass of 4.00.

So it appears that α-particles are helium atoms. However, there is an objection to this: we have said that α-particles, when first emitted, carry a charge of $+2e$, and the helium atoms collected in Figure 14.3 are neutral. But this difference can be reconciled by using what we learnt about ions in Section 13.1. A neutral helium atom that lacks two of its electrons is the ion He^{2+} with charge $+2e$. This is the α-particle that is first emitted from the radium atom. But it soon begins colliding with other atoms, with the walls of the container, or even with free electrons. In such collisions, the He^{2+} ion quickly picks up two electrons, and becomes one of the neutral helium atoms that we collected at the right of Figure 14.3. There is no contradiction. Radioactive processes in which α-particles are emitted are examples of α-**decay**. The α-particles that are initially produced in such radioactive processes are helium (He^{2+}) ions.

We can now see why radioactivity is so important. It involves the *transmutation* of an element, the dream of the medieval alchemist, which is epitomized by the fruitless attempt to turn lead into gold. True, the decay of radium only transmutes radium into radon and helium, but scientifically, it has the same standing. It shows that atoms are not eternal and indivisible as they were first assumed to be in Section 6.

Another characteristic of radioactive processes is that they are accompanied by large outputs of energy. For example, the Curies found that the temperature of a radium salt is always about 1.5 °C greater than that of its surroundings. To achieve this, each decay of an atom must release much more energy than would the reaction of an atom in a conventional chemical change, such as the combustion of carbon, in which atoms are neither created nor destroyed: each disintegration is an atomic explosion. Consequently, the particles fired off are moving very quickly; we shall now make use of this property.

14.3 Into the heart of the atom

From radium came the projectiles that tore aside the veil concealing the secret of atomic structure. The α-particles that radium emits are over 7 000 times more massive than the electron, and they are moving at about 15 000 kilometres per second. This enables them to penetrate atoms that they are fired at. Let us speculate on the fate of an invading α-particle of this sort.

What happens depends on the structure of atoms. Atoms, we believe, contain negatively charged electrons. The electron's mass is quite negligible compared with the mass of an atom, or even that of an α-particle, so where is the mass of an atom to be found? One possibility is that some or all of it is carried by the positively charged matter in the atom. Let us suppose that the electrons, and this positively charged matter, are fairly evenly spread throughout the space that the atom occupies. Now a swift-moving α-particle enters this space. Because of their tiny mass, any electrons that it encounters will be scattered like insects by a stone, and the α-particle will suffer little deflection from its course. But how about encounters with positively charged matter? Here we are handicapped by a lack of knowledge of its distribution.

However, positively charged α-particles emerge from some radioactive atoms. One possibility, therefore, is that the positively charged material is present in the form of α-particles, which are fairly evenly dispersed throughout the volume of the atom. To take one example, if nearly all of the mass of the atom is in the form of dispersed α-particles (relative atomic mass = 4.00), then a gold atom (relative atomic mass = 197) will contain 40–50 of them.

If so, then our invading α-particles will frequently encounter particles of similar mass and charge. They will behave somewhat like an ice-hockey puck struck hard in the direction of a group of other, stationary pucks on the same ice-rink. Figure 14.6 shows some possible outcomes. Experience tells us that the track of the moving puck will *never* be reversed by any collision with one of the stationary ones.*

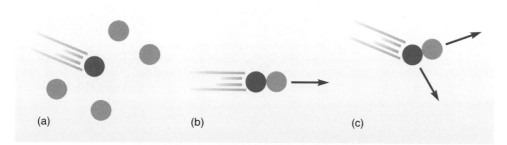

(a)   (b)   (c)

Figure 14.6 An ice-hockey puck moving through a region containing similar pucks. The moving puck may miss the others, (a). It may also collide with another puck and be stopped, (b), or suffer a forward deflection, (c). But it will *not* suffer a backward deflection.

An experiment of this type was first carried out at the suggestion of Ernest Rutherford (Figure 14.7). A narrow beam of α-particles from a radium source was directed at a thin piece of gold foil (Figure 14.8). Around the foil was placed a screen coated with zinc sulfide. This substance has the property of giving out a flash of light or *scintillation* when an α-particle strikes it. Thus individual α-particles can actually be counted by this scintillation method.

Figure 14.7 Ernest Rutherford (1871–1937) was a New Zealander who did research at Cambridge before moving, in 1898, to McGill University in Montreal. There he benefited from a splendid laboratory financed by a tobacco millionaire who thought smoking a disgusting habit. At McGill, Rutherford identified radioactivity with the decay of one element into another, before moving to Manchester in 1907 where he did the work that led to a model for the structure of the atom. When he returned to Cambridge in 1919, its Cavendish Laboratory became the world centre for experimental physics, producing a stream of Nobel Prize winners. Rutherford once said that there were two kinds of science: physics and crossword puzzles. This slightly marred his elation on receiving the Nobel Prize for Chemistry in 1908.

* You may rightly point out that such reversals sometimes occur with balls on a snooker table, but this is only because the incoming ball is cued to impart a rolling or spinning motion. Our choice of cylindrical pucks rules out this possibility.

Figure 14.8 Rutherford's gold foil experiment: the backward-deflected α-particles were the surprise. The experiment was performed in an evacuated chamber to prevent possible collisions of the α-particles with air molecules.

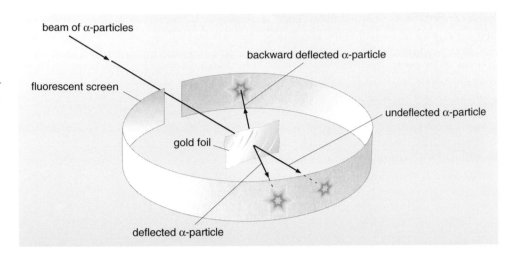

When two of Rutherford's colleagues did this experiment, they were surprised by two things. First of all, most α-particles passed through the foil without deflection.

⬤ What structural feature of atoms might explain this?

⚪ The atom is mainly empty space: most α-particles enjoy a totally uneventful passage.

The second surprise was that, contrary to the prediction of Figure 14.6, a few α-particles (about 1 in 8 000) were deflected by more than 90°: indeed in one or two cases, their course was almost entirely reversed. As the analogy of Figure 14.6 implies, such reversals are impossible if the mass and the positive charge are fairly evenly dispersed throughout the volume of the atom. Now Rutherford, like us, had started with the idea of just such an even dispersal, so he was astonished by these results. He afterwards wrote:

> It was quite the most incredible event that has ever happened to me in my life. It was almost as incredible as if you fired a 15-inch shell at a piece of tissue paper and it came back and hit you.

Rutherford now changed his ideas about the atom to accommodate the new results. Let's suppose that almost all of the mass of a gold atom, including the positively charged matter, is concentrated at its centre in a tiny volume. The atom is then largely empty space, so most invading α-particles miss this concentration of mass and positive charge, and pass straight through. This is consistent with the first surprise. It can also be squared with the second surprise, because when the α-particle *does* come up against the concentration of mass and positive charge at the centre of the gold atom, a reversal of course could occur. This is because like charges repel, so the α-particle will be thrown back by the increasing repulsion as it approaches the very high positive charge (Figure 14.9a). As Figure 14.9a implies, there is no actual collision, but because the concentration of positive charge is associated with a concentrated mass, the effect will be like that observed when a table-tennis ball is fired against a stationary cannonball (Figure 14.9b); the table-tennis ball rebounds, but the cannonball hardly stirs.

Rutherford called this tiny, positively charged concentration of mass the **atomic nucleus,** and assumed that it lay at the heart of the atom. This leads naturally to the famous **Rutherford model of the atom** (Figure 14.10). At its centre is a tiny

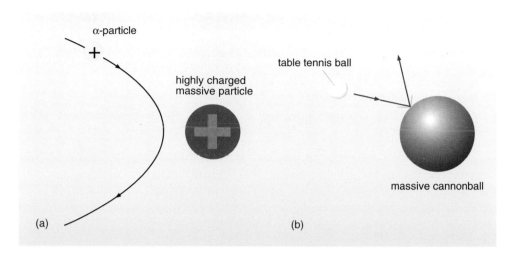

(a)

(b)

Figure 14.9 The backward deflection of positively charged α-particles in Figure 14.8 is explained by arguing that both the positive charge and nearly all of the mass of the gold atom are concentrated in a tiny volume. If an incoming α-particle encounters this very high positive charge, it is pushed back by the repulsion between like charges, and rebounds (a). Indeed, because the high positive charge at the centre of the gold atom is accompanied by a high mass, the changes in the speed and direction of the α-particle resemble those of a table-tennis ball when it encounters a cannonball (b).

positively charged nucleus, where nearly all the mass of the atom resides. Around this nucleus move electrons, each one with a single negative charge and a mass that is minute compared with that of the nucleus. They are in orbit, rather in the way that planets are in orbit around the Sun. Were it not for this motion, the electrons would be drawn into the nucleus by the attraction of the positive charge; in other words, the atom would collapse.

Figure 14.10 leaves some important questions unanswered. Consider, for example, a particular type of atom such as copper. How many electrons orbit the nucleus, and what total positive charge does that nucleus carry?

⬤ What can you say about these two unknown quantities?

◯ Each electron carries a negative charge, $-e$, and the atom is neutral. This can be so only if the positive charge on the nucleus is equal to the number of electrons multiplied by the charge $+e$.

By using other metal foils in the experiment of Figure 14.8, Rutherford and his colleagues were able to calculate the actual positive charges on the nuclei of some of the metal atoms. Taking the charge of the electron to be $-e$, they found, for example, in experiments with copper and silver foil, that the nuclear charges of the copper and silver atoms were $+29e$ and $+47e$, respectively.

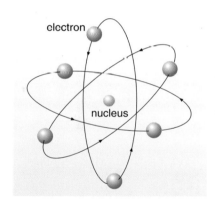

Figure 14.10   The Rutherford model of the atom.

⬤ Look back to the Periodic Table of Figure 12.6. What is the significance of the numbers 29 and 47 for copper and silver?

◯ They are equal to the serial numbers of the two elements in the Periodic Table.

This was a discovery of stunning importance: the serial number of a chemical element in the Periodic Table is equal, it seems, to the number of units of positive charge, $+e$, on the nucleus of its atom. This number is called the *atomic number* of the element. It is also equal to the number of electrons that orbit the nucleus in the neutral atom.

The atomic number is the fundamental quantity that distinguishes one chemical element from another. As you have progressed through this block, the definition of a chemical element has changed. To begin with, it was a substance that could not be broken down into chemical components (Section 4). Then it became a substance that contained just one type of atom (Section 6.6). Now it is a substance that is composed of atoms, each with the same characteristic number of positive charges, $+e$, on its nucleus.

14.4 Into the atomic nucleus

The paragraph that you have just read summarizes ideas that we have backed with much scientific evidence. They have carried us to the nucleus at the heart of the atom. Now we turn to the composition of the nucleus itself. Here, much of the scientific evidence is beyond the scope of this course. So the next two sections concentrate on *telling* you how things are; the supporting evidence will be less prominent than before.

Let's begin with the total positive charge on the nucleus. This exists because the nucleus contains tiny particles called **protons**. Each proton has a charge of $+e$, and a mass about 1 836 times that of an electron. Consider hydrogen, the first element in the Periodic Table. It has serial number one, so the charge on its atomic nucleus is $+e$.

⬤ How many protons does the nucleus of the hydrogen atom contain, and how many electrons are in orbit around this nucleus?

◯ Because a proton has a charge of $+e$, the total charge of $+e$ on the nucleus of the hydrogen atom indicates the presence of just *one* proton; as the atom is neutral, this nuclear charge of $+e$ must be balanced by the charge of $-e$ on *one* orbiting electron (Figure 14.11a).

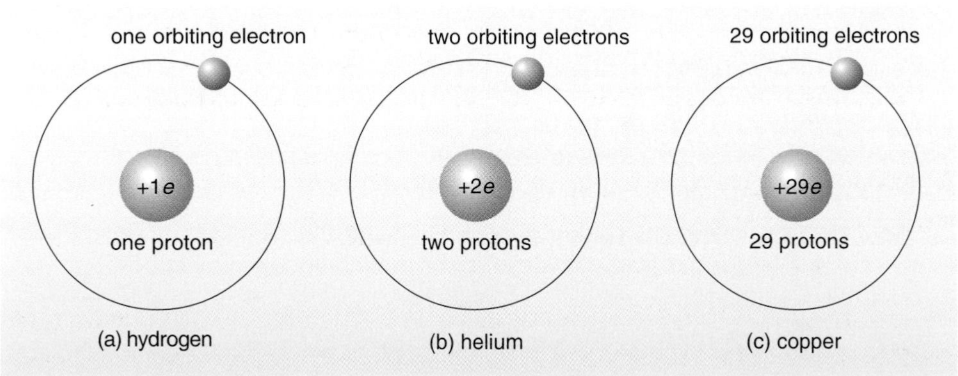

Figure 14.11 The number of protons in the nucleus, the total charge on the nucleus and the number of orbiting electrons in the neutral atoms of (a) hydrogen, (b) helium, and (c) copper.

one orbiting electron	two orbiting electrons	29 orbiting electrons
$+1e$	$+2e$	$+29e$
one proton	two protons	29 protons
(a) hydrogen	(b) helium	(c) copper

Notice how this sort of structure is consistent with our claim that virtually all the mass of an atom lies in its nucleus: each proton in the nucleus of an atom has a mass 1 836 times that of each orbiting electron.

⬤ What element comes after hydrogen in the Periodic Table? How many protons are there in its nucleus, and how many orbiting electrons in the neutral atom?

◯ Helium. With serial number 2 in the Periodic Table, helium atoms will have two protons in the nucleus, and two orbiting electrons (Figure 14.11b).

Thus it is very easy to find the number of protons in the nucleus, and the number of orbiting electrons in the atom from the position of an element in the Periodic Table. Copper, for example, has serial number or atomic number 29. So a copper atom has 29 orbiting electrons and 29 protons in its nucleus (Figure 14.11c). Indeed, this will be our final definition of the **atomic number** of an element: it is the number of protons in the nucleus of the atom. It is usually given the symbol Z. Thus for copper, $Z = 29$.

Now let us return to the helium and hydrogen atoms. Their masses reside in their nuclei. The helium nucleus contains two protons and the hydrogen nucleus has one.

What, by itself, does this suggest for the ratio of the masses of the helium and hydrogen atoms? Does this agree with the experimental values of the relative atomic masses, which are 4.0 and 1.0?

The helium nucleus contains just twice the number of protons in the hydrogen nucleus. By itself this suggests a mass ratio of 2 : 1. But the relative atomic masses reveal that the ratio is really 4 : 1.

The explanation of this discrepancy is the presence of a *third* type of particle, which is present in all nuclei except that of hydrogen. This particle carries no charge, has a mass almost identical with that of the proton, and is called the **neutron**. A helium nucleus contains two neutrons in addition to its two protons. So a hydrogen atom has just a single proton as its nucleus; a helium atom has two protons and two neutrons. As the masses of the proton and the neutron are virtually identical, the helium nucleus has a mass four times that of the hydrogen nucleus. Because the electrons in the atom have almost negligible mass, this ratio of 4 : 1 in the nuclear masses is very close to the ratio of atomic masses (Figure 14.12).

The nuclei of all atoms except those of hydrogen, therefore, consist of neutrons and protons. Let's call these nuclear particles, whether they are neutrons or protons, **nucleons**. A proton and a neutron have almost identical masses, so we can think of all nucleons as having the same mass. Our discussion has shown that it is the number of nucleons in a nucleus (the number of neutrons and protons) that determines the mass of an atom. We call this number the **mass number**. It is usually given the symbol A. As the hydrogen atom contains just one proton and no neutrons, its mass number is one: $A = 1$.

What is the mass number of the helium atom?

Four; the atom contains two protons and two neutrons, so the mass number is $(2 + 2)$; for the helium atom, $A = 4$.

We can embellish the symbol for an element so that it reveals the number of neutrons and protons in the nucleus of the atom. Against the symbol for the element, we write the atomic number as a preceding subscript, and the mass number as a preceding superscript. Thus the helium atom has atomic number 2, and mass number 4, so we write it $^{4}_{2}\text{He}$.

Figure 14.13 explains this symbolism by using sodium as an example. Let's use it to work out the numbers of protons, neutrons and orbiting electrons in the sodium atom. First we locate the atomic number; this is the preceding subscript, and here it takes the value 11. The atomic number is the number of protons in the nucleus; in the atom, it is also the number of orbiting electrons. Thus:

number of protons in the sodium atom = 11

number of electrons in the sodium atom = 11

Now we need the number of neutrons. To find this, we locate the mass number. This is the preceding superscript, and it takes the value 23 for sodium. The mass number is the number of nucleons in the nucleus so, in the sodium atom, there are 23 neutrons and protons. But we have already found that there are 11 protons, so the number of neutrons is $(23 - 11)$ or 12:

number of neutrons in the sodium atom = 12

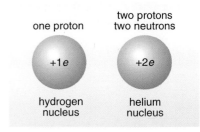

Figure 14.12   The total number of neutrons and protons in the helium nucleus is four times that in the hydrogen nucleus. The presence of the neutrons explains why the ratio of the masses of the atoms is 4 : 1, rather than 2 : 1 as Figure 14.11 would suggest.

Figure 14.13 A symbolism that tells us the numbers of neutrons, protons and electrons in the atom of an element.

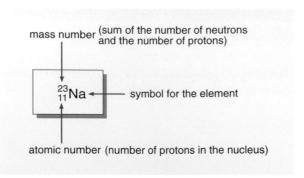

Notice that the number of neutrons is simply the mass number less the atomic number: the number of nucleons less the number of protons.

Question 14.1 For the fluorine atom, the symbol is $^{19}_{9}F$. Work out the number of protons, neutrons and electrons in the fluorine atom.◄

14.5 Isotopes

Our oxygen-16.0 scale of relative atomic masses is one on which hydrogen, which we now know carries one nucleon (one proton) in its nucleus, has a value of 1.0, to one decimal place. The helium nucleus, on the other hand, contains four nucleons (two protons and two neutrons), so the helium atom has a mass very close to four times that of the hydrogen atom: its relative atomic mass is 4.0. This brings us back to the surprise that we noted in Section 10: many chemical elements have relative atomic masses that are close to whole numbers. For example, to one decimal place, the values for hydrogen, helium, oxygen, fluorine and sodium are 1.0, 4.0, 16.0, 19.0 and 23.0, respectively.

⬤ Why is it no longer surprising that relative atomic masses are often close to whole numbers?

◯ Because, as the hydrogen and helium example shows, we unwittingly devised a scale on which each nucleon has a relative atomic mass very close to one. Now all atoms must have a whole number of nucleons in their nuclei. So the relative atomic mass of any particular atom should be very close to the whole number of nucleons in its nucleus. That whole number is the mass number.

This argument has completely inverted the problem. It is no longer surprising that relative atomic masses are often close to whole numbers. Our difficulty now is to explain why some of them are not; why copper, for example, has a relative atomic mass of 63.5. Once again, the nuclear atom provides an answer. The serial number of copper in the Periodic Table is 29; copper has an atomic number of 29. A copper atom, therefore, is one with a charge of $+29e$ on its nucleus or, what is the same thing, with 29 protons in the nucleus. Only then can it be copper. As the atom is neutral, it must also have 29 orbiting electrons.

Neither of these conditions, however, makes any demands about the number of *neutrons* in the copper atoms. All that an atom needs if it is to be copper is 29 protons in the nucleus. Once this condition is fulfilled, the number of neutrons is immaterial. If one atom has 29 protons and 34 neutrons in the nucleus, and another has 29 protons and 36 neutrons, they will both be atoms of copper. This is the actual situation that exists in the copper that you meet in everyday life. The copper wiring in your home contains both these types of atom.

○ Write chemical symbols, and attach the mass numbers and atomic numbers to these two types of atom.

○ $^{63}_{29}Cu$ and $^{65}_{29}Cu$, respectively: the atomic number is 29, which appears as a preceding subscript in both cases. The mass numbers of (29 + 34) and (29 + 36) are different and appear as preceding superscripts.

These two different kinds of atom are called isotopes of copper. **Isotopes** are atoms of the same chemical element that differ in the number of neutrons in their nuclei. They therefore have different mass numbers. Naturally occurring copper contains about 70% of $^{63}_{29}Cu$ and 30% of $^{65}_{29}Cu$. Thus the relative atomic mass of copper, which is 63.5, is an *average* mass: it lies between the two mass numbers of 63 and 65, but closer to 63 because that is the mass number of the more abundant isotope. Figure 14.14 summarizes information on the copper isotopes.

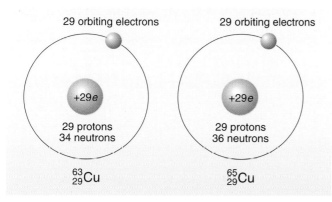

Figure 14.14 The distribution of protons, neutrons and electrons in the atoms of the two isotopes of copper present in copper metal. In both cases, the atomic number is 29: there are 29 protons in the nucleus. This means that both types are atoms of copper, but they differ in the number of neutrons.

When copper is taken through the cycle of chemical reactions that we studied in Section 3, the two types of copper atom behave in almost exactly the same way. Whether copper metal is made up of $^{63}_{29}Cu$ or $^{65}_{29}Cu$ atoms or of a mixture of the two makes virtually no difference. It is red and forms black copper oxide, CuO, when heated in oxygen. Isotopes are very nearly identical *chemically*.

We conclude that the usual reason why an element has a relative atomic mass close to a whole number is that it consists mainly or entirely of just one isotope. For example, natural hydrogen is 99.85% $^{1}_{1}H$, natural carbon is 98.9% $^{12}_{6}C$, natural oxygen is 99.8% $^{16}_{8}O$ and natural fluorine is 100% $^{19}_{9}F$. Elements whose relative atomic masses differ from whole numbers by more than ±0.1 contain significant proportions of at least two isotopes. Thus chlorine, relative atomic mass 35.5, is about 75% $^{35}_{17}Cl$ and 25% $^{37}_{17}Cl$.[*]

---

[*] This point can be reinforced by introducing the internationally agreed scale of relative atomic masses. In Section 10, we said that this was very slightly different from the oxygen-16 scale that we have been using. The international scale is one on which the isotope of carbon, $^{12}_{6}C$, is given the value 12. It therefore cannot be understood without the concept of isotopes, and this is why we have delayed its introduction for so long. On this scale, natural carbon has a value, to four significant figures, of 12.01. This is because, although $^{12}_{6}C$ is given the value 12, natural carbon also contains 1.1% of the isotope $^{13}_{6}C$. Natural carbon therefore has a relative atomic mass slightly greater than 12. As we promised in Section 10, to four significant figures, the international scale and our oxygen-16 scale give identical relative atomic masses.

14.5.1 The nature of α-decay

The symbolism of Sections 14.4 and 14.5 can be used to reveal the essence of α-decay. The radium that Marie Curie extracted from uranium ores consists of the isotope with mass number 226. When it emits an α-particle, it forms the radon isotope of mass number 222. These mass numbers correspond to the relative atomic masses quoted in Section 14.2.1.

The atomic numbers of radium and radon are 88 and 86, respectively, and the α-particle that is emitted is the helium isotope $^4_2$He. Thus the α-decay of radium can be written:

$$^{226}_{88}\text{Ra} \longrightarrow \,^{222}_{86}\text{Rn} + \,^4_2\text{He} \tag{14.1}$$

This equation tells us about changes in the *nuclei* of atoms: a radium nucleus becomes a radon nucleus by losing two protons and two neutrons in the form of an α-particle. The surrounding electrons of the atoms in Equation 14.1 are ignored, and attention is focused on changes in the nuclei; α-decay is an example of a **nuclear reaction**.

Nuclear reactions differ from chemical reactions in that atoms are *not* conserved: in Equation 14.1, radium appears on one side of the equation, and radon and helium on the other. So what *is* conserved in nuclear reactions? The answer is mass number and charge.

⬤ How does the conservation of mass number reveal itself in Equation 14.1?

◯ The sum of the mass numbers of the reactants (226) is equal to that of the products (222 + 4).

To see that there is charge conservation, we pick out the charged particles in the equation. Here, these are the protons in the nuclei, each of which has a charge of $+e$. There are 88 protons in the nucleus of the radium atom that decays, and (86 + 2) in the radon and helium nuclei that are produced: the charges sum to $+88e$ on each side of the equation.

Finally, Equation 14.1 reveals the essential nature of α-decay: the decaying nucleus loses an α-particle ($^4_2$He), so its mass number decreases by four and its atomic number by two.

14.6 How big is a zillion?

Moles of chemical substances all contain the same number of formula units, and in Section 10.2 we called this number *one zillion* because we do not yet know exactly how large it is. We are now ready to find out, but let us first remind you what a mole is. Carbon dioxide contains CO_2 molecules. The sum of the relative atomic masses for this formula unit is 44.0. We follow this number by the symbol for the gram. Thus one mole of CO_2 molecules is 44.0 g of carbon dioxide. Likewise, helium gas consists of helium *atoms*, He, with a relative atomic mass of 4.00. One mole of He is 4.00 g of helium. 44.0 g of carbon dioxide contains one zillion CO_2 molecules and 4.00 g of helium contains one zillion He atoms; the number of formula units is the same in both cases, but how big is it?

Box 14.2, *Counting the zillion,* describes an experiment that was designed by Rutherford to answer the question. It gave a value of 6.2×10^{23} for the number of helium atoms in one mole of helium gas. Now the number of formula units per mole is the same for all chemical substances. So Rutherford's work suggests that this quantity is about 6.2×10^{23} mol^{-1}, where we have used the symbol 'mol' as shorthand for the mole.

> The number of formula units per mole of a chemical substance is called the **Avogadro constant**, after Amadeo Avogadro of Section 8.1, and given the symbol N_A. Accurate determinations by modern methods give
> $N_A = 6.02 \times 10^{23}$ mol^{-1}.

The unit mol^{-1} indicates that N_A is a number of formula units *per mole* of a chemical substance. Thus one zillion is 6.02×10^{23}: there are 6.02×10^{23} CO_2 molecules in 44.0 g of carbon dioxide, and 6.02×10^{23} helium atoms in 4.00 g of helium. The number is, of course, enormous: six followed by 23 zeros. If helium atoms were glass marbles 1 cm across, and if these were laid out in contact in a straight line, then the 6×10^{23} atoms in 4.00 g of helium would stretch for a distance of over 600 000 light years. This is about six times the width of our galaxy, and about one-quarter of the distance to the Andromeda galaxy, the most distant object visible to the naked eye.

Box 14.2   Counting the zillion

Rutherford's measurement of the Avogadro constant started with the experiment in Figure 14.15. Its purpose was to find the number of α-particles emitted by 1 g of radium in one year. A tiny source containing an α-particle emitter prepared from radium was suspended in a long cylindrical glass tube, at the end of which was a small circular hole leading to a chamber where α-particles could be detected and counted. The whole apparatus was evacuated to prevent collisions between the emitted α-particles and air molecules.

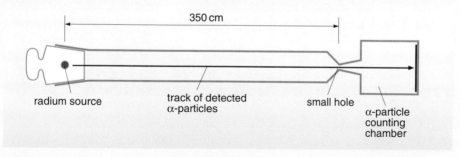

350 cm

radium source   track of detected   small hole   α-particle
                       α-particles   counting
                                                                      chamber

Figure 14.15   A schematic diagram of an experiment designed to count the α-particles emitted by radium.

Rather than getting bogged down in the detailed calculations, we shall just try to give you an idea of the numbers that are involved. In one experiment, Rutherford found that when the source contained the equivalent of 0.039 mg of radium, and the hole had a radius of 0.062 cm, then 25 α-particles passed into the counting chamber in 10 minutes. Scaling these data up, we find that if the source contained 1 g of radium, then in one year 3.4×10^{10} α-particles should enter the counting chamber.

Figure 14.16 A radium source, placed at the centre of a spherical shell of radius 350 cm, fires off α-particles in all directions. Those detected in Figure 14.15 are the number fired through a tiny hole, A, of radius 0.062 cm, on the surface of the sphere. By scaling this number up from the area of the hole to the much larger area of the spherical surface, one finds the *total* number of α-particles emitted by the radium.

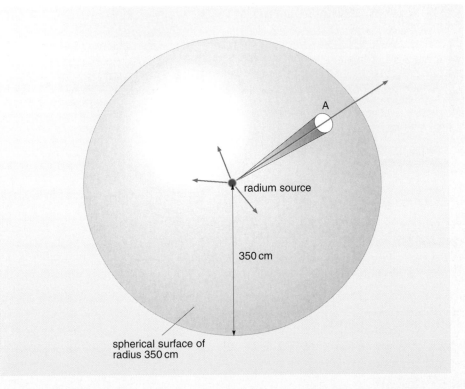

This, however, is only the tiny fraction of α-particles that pass through the hole. What is the *total* number emitted? The distance from the source to the hole is 350 cm, so around the source we draw an imaginary sphere at a radius of 350 cm (Figure 14.16). All the α-particles fired off by 1 g of radium in one year will pass through this spherical surface. Now we draw a tiny circle of radius 0.062 cm on the surface. We know that through this hole, 3.4×10^{10} α-particles have passed. All we need to do now is to scale this number up from the area of the hole to the area of the spherical surface. This gives a value of 4.3×10^{18} α-particles.

Now you know from Section 14.2.1 that these α-particles end up as helium gas. In a separate experiment, Rutherford measured how much helium gas is produced by 1 g of radium in one year. It was just 0.156 cm³ at STP. This has a mass of only 2.79×10^{-5} g, and it must be the mass of the 4.3×10^{18} atoms of helium produced by the 4.3×10^{18} α-particles which were emitted in the same time. So:

2.79×10^{-5} g of helium contains 4.3×10^{18} atoms

1 g of helium contains $\dfrac{4.3 \times 10^{18}}{2.79 \times 10^{-5}}$ atoms

One *mole* of helium atoms has a mass of 4.00 g, so:

one mole of helium atoms contains $\dfrac{4.00 \times 4.3 \times 10^{18}}{2.79 \times 10^{-5}}$ atoms

$= 6.2 \times 10^{23}$ atoms.

14.7 How small is an atom?

Our value for the Avogadro constant will give us an idea of the size of an atom. Let's use gold as an example. The relative atomic mass of gold is 197, so one mole of gold atoms has a mass of about 200 g. Now gold is a dense metal: each cubic centimetre has a mass of about 20 g, so one mole of gold occupies a volume of about 10 cm^3, which is 10^{-5} m^3. This volume, therefore, contains 6×10^{23} gold atoms:

6×10^{23} gold atoms occupy 10^{-5} m^3

so 1 gold atom occupies $\dfrac{10^{-5}}{6 \times 10^{23}}$ m^3

$= 1.7 \times 10^{-29}$ m^3

Let us think of this tiny volume dedicated to each gold atom as a cube. What is the length of its side? It is the length which, when multiplied by itself, and then by itself again, gives the volume of 1.7×10^{-29} m^3. This length is 2.6×10^{-10} m. You could set about 30 million gold atoms in a line across your finger nail.

So atoms are tiny; they can never be seen with the naked eye, or even with the best optical microscope. Yet we have managed to work out their approximate size. Recently, a technique has been developed that gets much closer to giving us actual images of atoms on a surface. This is called scanning tunnelling microscopy, and you saw one example of what it can do in Figure 1.1. Figure 14.17a provides a similar kind of image for a layer of gold atoms. Figure 14.17b shows a model of this layer supplied by a computer graphics package. The distance across a gold atom is 2.88×10^{-10} m: the estimate that we obtained above is pretty good.

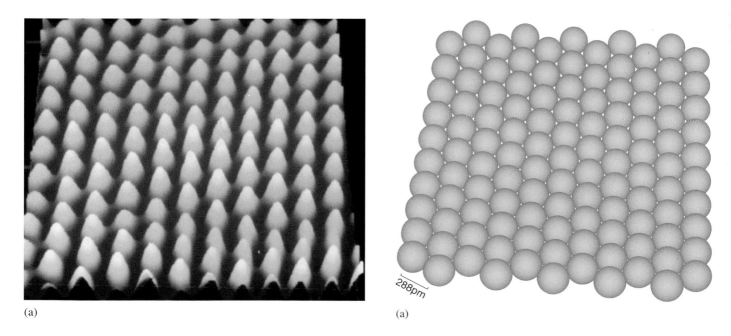

(a)   (a)

Figure 14.17 (a) An image of the layer of gold atoms on the surface of a crystal; (b) a computer-generated model of the same layer showing the distance spanned by a gold atom. As 1 pm is 1 picometre, which is 10^{-12} m, 288 picometres are 288×10^{-12} m, or 2.88×10^{-10} m.

14.8 Summary of Section 14

The main points of Section 14 are as follows:

1   Uranium and its compounds are radioactive: that is, they emit radiation that fogs a photographic plate.

2   The radiation is of three kinds: γ-rays, which are not deflected when passed between the poles of a powerful magnet; negatively charged β-particles, which *are* deflected and turn out to be fast-moving electrons; and the much more massive, positively charged α-particles, which are deflected in the opposite direction to the electrons.

3   Radium compounds, which were first discovered and extracted in visible amounts by Marie and Pierre Curie, are a very intense source of α-particles. Radium salts gradually produce two noble gases: radon, which is itself radioactive, and helium. The helium comes directly from the emitted α-particles, which are fast-moving He^{2+} ions. These ions gain electrons very soon after emission, and become He atoms.

4   Individual α-particles can be detected as scintillations when they strike a screen coated in zinc sulfide. Rutherford bombarded a thin gold foil surrounded by such a screen with α-particles from radium and used the scintillations to detect how the particles were scattered. Nearly all suffered little or no deviation, but about one in 8 000 were driven back towards the radium source, and some of these even reversed course.

5   From this, Rutherford deduced that the atom was nearly all empty space. Its positive charge, and virtually all its mass, are concentrated in a tiny nucleus. Orbiting this nucleus are electrons, each with a single negative charge, $-e$, and the number of electrons is equal to the number of positive charges, $+e$, on the nucleus. Overall, therefore, the atom is electrically neutral.

6   The number of positive charges on the nucleus is equal to the serial number of the element in the Periodic Table. This number of positive charges on the nucleus is called the atomic number of the element. It is what distinguishes one chemical element from another. The positive charge exists because the nucleus contains particles called protons, each of which has a charge of $+e$ and a mass nearly 2 000 times that of the electron.

7   The atomic number is therefore simultaneously:

•   the number of positive charges on the nucleus;

•   the number of protons in the nucleus;

•   the number of electrons in the *neutral* atom;

•   what distinguishes one chemical element from another; all atoms of a particular element have the same atomic number;

•   the correct ordering parameter for putting elements in the Periodic Table; Mendeléev succeeded because the order of relative atomic masses happens usually to be the same as the order of atomic numbers.

8   The helium atom has twice as many protons in its nucleus as the hydrogen atom, but its mass is four times as great. This is because all nuclei except that of hydrogen contain a second type of particle alongside the protons. This is the neutron; it carries no charge and has a mass very similar to that of the proton. A helium nucleus contains two protons and two neutrons.

9   The protons and neutrons in the nuclei of atoms are given the general name of nucleons. The mass number of an atom is the number of nucleons in its nucleus.

10   All atoms of an element must contain the same number of protons, but they may differ in the number of neutrons. This gives rise to atoms of an element with the same atomic number but different mass numbers. These different types of atom are called isotopes. In chemical changes they behave almost identically.

11   In α-decay, the loss of the α-particle by the decaying isotope leads to a decrease of four in the mass number, and a decrease of two in the atomic number.

12   The number we have called a zillion — the number of formula units in one mole of a chemical substance — is called the Avogadro constant, N_A, and has the value $N_A = 6.02 \times 10^{23}$ mol^{-1}. This suggests that atoms are a few hundred picometres across (1 pm = 10^{-12} m).

It is important that you fully understand the equality of the atomic number of an element with its serial number in the Periodic Table, the number of protons in its nucleus, and the number of orbiting electrons in the neutral atom. Equally important is the relationship between the mass number of a particular isotope, its atomic number and the number of neutrons in its nucleus. Remember also that the mass number of the isotope is equal to that isotope's relative atomic mass rounded to the nearest whole number. Thus beryllium, Be, the fourth element in the Periodic Table, contains just one isotope and has atomic mass 9.01. So the mass number of the isotope is 9, its atomic number is 4, and it is written $^9_4$Be. These and other skills are tested in Questions 14.1–14.4. Question 14.5 does this too, and makes sure that you can write examples of α-decay. Finally, Question 14.6 revises your understanding of the mole concept by asking you to use the Avogadro constant to convert fractions and multiples of moles into numbers of formula units.

Question 14.2   Aluminium has a relative atomic mass of 27.0, and contains just one isotope. Use the mini Periodic Table in Figure 12.7 to:

(a) Deduce the number of protons in the aluminium nucleus;

(b) Deduce the number of orbiting electrons in the neutral aluminium atom;

(c) Deduce the number of neutrons in the aluminium nucleus;

(d) Write down the symbol for the isotope that is present in aluminium by correctly combining its mass number and atomic number with the symbol for aluminium.◀

Question 14.3   Uranium contains two isotopes, $^{235}_{92}$U and $^{238}_{92}$U. In natural uranium there is 0.7% $^{235}_{92}$U and 99.3% $^{238}_{92}$U.

(a) How many protons are there in the nuclei of $^{235}_{92}$U and $^{238}_{92}$U?

(b) How many neutrons are there in the nuclei of $^{235}_{92}$U and $^{238}_{92}$U?

(c) From mere inspection of the isotope abundances, what is the relative atomic mass of natural uranium to the nearest whole number?◀

Question 14.4 Table 14.1 shows the nuclear composition of four pairs of atoms.

(a) Which pairs of atoms are atoms of the same element?

(b) With the help of the Periodic Table in Figure 12.6, confirm your answer by writing the symbol, complete with mass number and atomic number, for each of the eight atoms. ◄

Table 14.1 For use with Question 14.4.

	First atom of pair		Second atom of pair	
	Protons	Neutrons	Protons	Neutrons
pair 1	18	22	19	21
pair 2	18	18	18	20
pair 3	20	20	20	22
pair 4	94	145	90	145

Question 14.5 The radon isotope $^{222}_{86}\text{Rn}$, which is produced in the α-decay shown in Equation 14.1, also undergoes α-decay. So does the commonest isotope of uranium, $^{238}_{92}\text{U}$. Use the Periodic Table of Figure 12.6 to identify the isotopes that are produced, and write equations for the reactions. ◄

Question 14.6 In this question, you should use the relative atomic masses in Appendix 1, and the value $N_A = 6.02 \times 10^{23}$ mol^{-1}.

(a) How many oxygen atoms are there in 32.0 g of oxygen gas?

(b) How many oxygen molecules, O_2, are there in 32.0 g of oxygen gas?

(c) How many oxygen atoms and how many calcium atoms are there in 28.05 g of quicklime, CaO?

(d) How many gold atoms are there in 1.970 g of gold?

(e) How many sodium atoms and how many sulfur atoms are there in 312.4 g of sodium sulfide, Na_2S?

(f) How many aluminium atoms and how many oxygen atoms are there in 153.0 g of aluminium oxide, Al_2O_3? ◄

Final thoughts

15

In this block, you have penetrated deeply into the world of the atom. Although atoms are far too small to be seen, even with the most powerful optical microscope, we have nevertheless, by a combination of experiments, inspired guesswork and logic, been able to weigh them, to estimate their size, and even to find out what they are made of. The route we followed was to take the world apart, first into about 100 chemical elements, then into about 100 different types of atom, and finally into just three kinds of particle: protons, neutrons and electrons. This pathway has brought scientists to a world in which, today, individual atoms can be manipulated on surfaces. You saw examples of this in Figures 1.1 and 14.17a; Figure 15.1 now shows you another.

Figure 15.1 An image of a ring of 48 iron atoms on a copper surface, produced using scanning tunnelling microscopy. Notice the wave-like crests and troughs inside the ring. These are thought to be due to electrons confined within the ring. As you will see in Block 7, confined electrons have some wave-like properties.

Take a little time to think how we made our way. We made sense of what we noticed or found out by constructing theories and models. These constructs then pointed the way to new experiments, through which our understanding made a further advance. At all times, however, it was important not to treat theories with exaggerated respect. We did not hesitate to reconstruct them when new discoveries demanded it. Thus we persevered for many pages with an atomic theory that claimed atoms to be indestructible. Eventually we found that this could not be squared with radioactivity: some atoms spontaneously come apart, and it was this realization that enabled us to reason our way inside the atom. Again, our original atomic theory claimed that atoms of the same element were identical. The discovery of isotopes showed that this was not the case: they may seem chemically identical, but they differ in mass. To repeat the metaphor of Box 6.1, science advances when scientific practice exposes a weakness in scientific theory.

Finally, unfinished business: chemical elements differ from one another because of differences in atomic number. The atomic number is the number of protons in the nucleus. But it is also equal to the number of electrons that surround the nucleus in the neutral atom. This leaves an unanswered question of great importance. Neon atoms contain 10 electrons, argon atoms 18 electrons and potassium atoms 19 electrons. We are saying that these differences in number explain why the three elements are distinct. But neon and argon are in fact very similar to one another, and *very* different from potassium. Why? The answer lies in the way that the electrons are arranged around the nucleus. This is the next stage of the story and it is taken up in Block 7. Then, in Block 8, we shall be able to show you how the Periodic Table can be explained in terms of the arrangement of electrons within the atoms of the chemical elements.

 Activity 15.1   *Reviewing your study of Block 6: techniques for understanding*

This activity asks you to review your learning, along with the procedures that you used when you got stuck. ◀

Questions: answers and comments

Comments on the answers are given in curly brackets {...}.

Question 2.1   The required word reaction is:

sodium chloride + sulfuric acid ⟶
  sodium hydrogen sulfate + hydrogen chloride

From Section 2.2.1, the white solid left when the reaction is over is sodium hydrogen sulfate. The *reactants* appear on the left-hand side of the reaction separated by a plus sign. These substances wholly or partly disappear during the reaction and are replaced by products. The arrow points from the reactants to the *products*, which are separated by a plus sign on the right-hand side of the reaction.

Question 2.2   You have met, in a different context, two substances that absorb water vigorously. These are concentrated sulfuric acid (Sections 2.1.1 and 2.3.1) and calcium chloride (Section 2.4.2). They are both used in desiccators.

Question 2.3   The priority will be to obtain fresh water from salt water by *distillation*. The retort and the gas burner are the items that will allow you to do this (Figure 2.11).

Question 2.4   Place the mixture in a beaker, add water and stir vigorously. The salt dissolves but the sand does not. *Filtration* therefore separates the sand, which is caught in the filter paper, from a solution of the salt, which passes through. If the solution is then warmed or left open to the air, *evaporation* occurs and the salt *crystallizes* from the solution.

Question 2.5   The whole point of the sulfuric acid bubbler would be lost if the positions of the bottles were exchanged. The sulfuric acid is acting as a drying agent. If, after drying, the gas were passed through water, it would simply get wet again. So the sequence must be water first to remove hydrogen chloride gas, and sulfuric acid next to remove water.

Question 2.6   As vinegar turns blue litmus red, it is an acid. It should therefore also react with limestone to give carbon dioxide, and with magnesium to give hydrogen. And it does, although the reactions are fairly slow.

Question 3.1   The missing masses in Table 3.2 are:

mass of copper powder = 1.500 g

mass of copper oxide = 1.878 g

They are obtained by subtracting the mass of the empty boat (10.486 g) first from the mass of the boat when loaded with copper (11.986 g) and second from the mass of the boat when that copper has become copper oxide (12.364 g). Thus, 1.878 g of copper oxide contain 1.500 g of copper and 0.378 g of oxygen, the latter being the difference between the masses of copper oxide and copper. So the percentage of copper in copper oxide is

$$\frac{1.500\,g}{1.878\,g} \times 100\% = 79.9\%$$

and the percentage of oxygen in copper oxide is

$$\frac{0.378\,g}{1.878\,g} \times 100\% = 20.1\%$$

Thus despite the change in the starting mass of copper, the percentage composition of copper oxide (79.9% copper, 20.1% oxygen) turns out the same as before. Note how this arises in the arithmetic. The mass of copper taken (1.500 g) is 50% greater than before, and the mass of copper oxide obtained (1.878 g) turns out to be also 50% greater than before.

Question 4.1   The difference between the mass of lead oxide (1.077 g) and the mass of lead at the start of the experiment (1.000 g) is the mass of oxygen that was taken up by the lead. This is 0.077 g. Thus 1.077 g of orange lead oxide is composed of 1.000 g of lead and 0.077 g of oxygen. So the percentage of lead in lead oxide is

$$\frac{1.000\,g}{1.077\,g} \times 100\% = 92.9\%$$

and the percentage of oxygen in lead oxide is

$$\frac{0.077\,g}{1.077\,g} \times 100\% = 7.1\%$$

Question 4.2   The difference between the mass of silver chloride that was formed (0.753 g) and the initial mass of silver (0.567 g) is 0.186 g. This is the mass of chlorine taken up. Thus 0.753 g of silver chloride is composed of 0.567 g of silver and 0.186 g of chlorine. So the percentage of silver in silver chloride is

$$\frac{0.567\,g}{0.753\,g} \times 100\% = 75.3\%$$

and the percentage of chlorine in silver chloride is

$$\frac{0.186\,g}{0.753\,g} \times 100\% = 24.7\%$$

Question 4.3 (a) Iron (Fe) and sulfur (S); (b) aluminium (Al) and bromine (Br); (c) zinc (Zn), nitrogen (N) and oxygen (O); (d) sodium (Na), bromine and oxygen; (e) sodium, hydrogen (H), sulfur and oxygen; (f) calcium (Ca) and carbon (C).

{The names reveal the constituent elements very clearly if one remembers the proviso that the ending -ate indicates the presence of oxygen *in addition to* the more obvious components. Remember that the ending -ide usually marks a compound of just two elements, the first of which is often a metal, and the second, to which the ending is attached, is a non-metal.}

Question 4.4 The only possibility is combination (b). Table 4.1 shows that nitric acid is composed of hydrogen, nitrogen and oxygen. None of the substances in combinations (a) and (c) contains nitrogen so they are unsuitable. {In fact, nitric acid can be made industrially from air, which is chiefly nitrogen and oxygen gases, and water, which contains hydrogen, but it is now more common to use natural gas as the source of hydrogen.}

Question 6.1 (a) CuO; the metallic element is written first; this has the meaning Cu_1O_1, the ones being understood (see Section 6.2).

(b) If CuO is the correct formula then 1.000 g of copper and 0.252 g of oxygen must contain the same number of atoms. Let's call this same number one tillion. Then the mass of a copper atom is 1.000 tillionths of a gram and the mass of an oxygen atom is 0.252 tillionths of a gram. The ratio is 1.000 : 0.252 or 3.97 : 1.

(c) Red copper oxide is composed of 88.8% copper and 11.2% oxygen. So, in 100 g of red copper oxide:

11.2 g of oxygen are combined with 88.8 g of copper

1.00 g of oxygen is combined with $\dfrac{88.8\,g}{11.2}$ of copper

0.252 g of oxygen is combined with $\dfrac{0.252 \times 88.8\,g}{11.2}$ of copper

which works out to 2.00 g of copper.

Thus, in black copper oxide, 0.252 g of oxygen is combined with 1.000 g of copper, and in red copper oxide it is combined with twice this mass. So if every oxygen atom is combined with one copper atom in black copper oxide, it must be combined with two copper atoms in red copper oxide, whose formula is therefore Cu_2O.

Question 6.2 The ratio between the numbers of hydrogen, sulfur and oxygen atoms is 2 : 1 : 4. The formula contains four oxygen and two hydrogen atoms, so the ratio of oxygen to hydrogen atoms is 2 : 1. There are two oxygen atoms for every hydrogen atom.

Question 6.3 The names and formulae are: magnesium dichloride, $MgCl_2$; aluminium trichloride, $AlCl_3$; and dialuminium trioxide, Al_2O_3. Again, the metallic elements are written first in the formulae by convention.

Question 6.4 The equation is not balanced because there are different numbers of iron and chlorine atoms on each side of the equation. There are two iron atoms on the left side, and only one on the right; there are three chlorine atoms on the left side and only two on the right. If a 2 is placed before $FeCl_3$ on the left, and a 3 before $FeCl_2$ on the right, there are then six chlorine atoms on each side — the equation is balanced with respect to chlorine:

$$Fe(s) + 2FeCl_3(s) \longrightarrow 3FeCl_2(s)$$

By chance, the equation is now also balanced with respect to iron: there are three iron atoms on each side.

Question 7.1 It will be greater; the height of the water should be 10.3 m (about 34 feet).

As water is much less dense than mercury, the atmospheric pressure can support a much taller column of water. If we imagine columns of water and mercury with the same cross-section and the same mass, then as the density of mercury is 13.6 times that of water, the height of the water column will be 13.6 times that of the mercury column. Thus if atmospheric pressure supports 760 mm of mercury; it will support (760 × 13.6) mm of water. This is 10 300 mm or 10.3 m of water (about 34 feet). It is much greater than the height of the mercury column.

Question 7.2 (a) When the submarine first hit bottom at 40 m, there was atmospheric pressure plus 40 m of water bearing down on the hatch and only atmospheric pressure pressing up from inside. But as water gradually entered the breached hull, the internal pressure increased towards that immediately outside the boat. Eventually, therefore, Wenniger's efforts from inside opened the hatch.

(b) When Wenniger left the hatch, the external pressure acting on the air in his lungs would have been that experienced at 40 m depth. As he rose, this external pressure decreased so the air in his lungs expanded (Boyle's law) and he felt forced to exhale.

(c) Because the small volume of air in it expanded as it rose (see (b) above).

(d) Unlike Wenniger, who came up slowly and exhaled as he went, these men came up quickly without exhaling. The rapid expansion of the air burst their lungs.

(e) From Question 7.1, atmospheric pressure is equivalent to that exerted by a column of water 10.3 m high. So the pressure experienced 40 m below the surface of the sea is that exerted by a column of water about $(10 + 40)$ m or 50 m high. This is about five times atmospheric pressure.

Question 7.3 (a) 840 mmHg; (b) 840 mmHg; (c) 680 mmHg. In each case, the pressure at the mercury surface C in the open arm of the tube is 760 mm of mercury, and the pressure of the gas in the bulb is that at its adjacent mercury surface, A. In (a) and (b), the pressure at A is the same as that at B because A and B are at the same level and there is an uninterrupted pathway between the two through mercury. As B lies 80 mm below C, the pressure at B, and therefore in the bulb, is $(760 + 80)$ or 840 mm. In (c), the pressure at C (760 mm) is equal to that at D which lies 80 mm below A. So

pressure at A + 80 mmHg = 760 mmHg

The pressure at A (in the bulb) is therefore $(760 − 80)$ mmHg, or 680 mmHg.

Question 7.4 As in Activity 7.2, we apply Boyle's and Charles' laws in turn. Applying Boyle's law first at 100 °C:

760 mmHg × (volume at 760 mmHg) =
$$1\,000 \text{ mmHg} \times 760 \text{ cm}^3$$

Dividing both sides by 760 mmHg:

$$\text{volume at 760 mmHg} = \frac{1000 \text{ mmHg} \times 760 \text{ cm}^3}{760 \text{ mmHg}}$$

$$= 1\,000 \text{ cm}^3$$

Now 0 °C is 273 K, and 100 °C is $(273 + 100)$ K or 373 K. Applying Charles' law at 760 mmHg:

$$\frac{\text{volume at 273 K}}{273 \text{ K}} = \frac{\text{volume at 373 K}}{373 \text{ K}} = \frac{1\,000 \text{ cm}^3}{373 \text{ K}}$$

$$\text{volume at 273 K} = \frac{1\,000 \text{ cm}^3 \times 273 \text{ K}}{373 \text{ K}} = 732 \text{ cm}^3$$

At STP, this gas sample has a volume of 732 cm³.

Question 7.5 In the case of hydrogen,

$$\text{volume} = \frac{\text{mass}}{\text{density}} = \frac{0.0276 \text{ g}}{0.0899 \text{ g litre}^{-1}} = 0.307 \text{ litre}$$

The calculations for chlorine and hydrogen chloride are similar, and give volumes of 0.308 litre and 0.613 litre, respectively. Thus the volumes of hydrogen, chlorine and hydrogen chloride are almost exactly in the ratio 1 : 1 : 2 observed in the experiment of Figure 7.19.

Question 8.1 From the composition of water:

11.2 g of hydrogen are combined with 88.8 g of oxygen

so 1.00 g of hydrogen is combined with $\dfrac{88.8 \text{ g}}{11.2}$ of oxygen

= 7.93 g of oxygen

Thus, in water, 1.00 g of hydrogen is combined with 7.93 g of oxygen.

As the formula is H_2O, 1.00 g of hydrogen contains twice as many atoms as 7.93 g of oxygen. If there are one zillion atoms in 1.00 g of hydrogen, there are half a zillion atoms in 7.93 g of oxygen. This means that there are one zillion oxygen atoms in $(2 \times 7.93 \text{ g})$ or 15.9 g of oxygen. So 1.00 g of hydrogen and 15.9 g of oxygen contain the same number of atoms. The ratio of the mass of an oxygen atom to that of a hydrogen atom is 15.9 : 1.00, or 16 : 1.0 to two significant figures. To two significant figures, then, an oxygen atom has a mass sixteen times that of a hydrogen atom.

Question 8.2

2 volumes carbon monoxide + 1 volume oxygen

$\longrightarrow$ 2 volumes carbon dioxide

Replacing *volume* by *molecule* (Avogadro's hypothesis) gives:

2 molecules carbon monoxide + 1 molecule oxygen

$\longrightarrow$ 2 molecules carbon dioxide

The formulae of the molecules of carbon monoxide, oxygen and carbon dioxide (Table 8.2) are CO, O_2 and CO_2, respectively, so the chemical equation is:

$$2CO(g) + O_2(g) \longrightarrow 2CO_2(g)$$

This is balanced: there are two carbon atoms and four oxygen atoms in the reactants and in the product. {Note the use of the letter g in parentheses to indicate that each reactant and product is in the gaseous state.}

Question 8.3   The two molecules of ammonia, $2NH_3$, contain two nitrogen and six hydrogen atoms. Table 8.2 shows that nitrogen gas consists of N_2 molecules and hydrogen gas of H_2 molecules, so when the two ammonia molecules decompose, the two nitrogen atoms will end up as an N_2 molecule, and the six hydrogen atoms as three H_2 molecules. So the balanced equation is:

$$2NH_3(g) \longrightarrow N_2(g) + 3H_2(g)$$

From Avogadro's hypothesis, we know that the words *molecule* and *volume* are interchangeable for gas reactions of this type, so when the reaction occurs:

$$\text{2 volumes ammonia} \longrightarrow \text{1 volume nitrogen +}$$
$$\text{3 volumes hydrogen}$$

Thus 2 volumes of ammonia give 4 volumes of a mixture of nitrogen and hydrogen — the total volume of gas doubles. One quarter of the doubled volume is nitrogen; the rest is hydrogen.

Question 8.4   As ammonia is NH_3, 1.0 g of hydrogen must contain three times as many atoms as does 4.6 g of nitrogen. So 1.0 g of hydrogen and 13.8 g of nitrogen must contain the *same* number of atoms. Thus the ratio of the masses of the hydrogen and nitrogen atoms is 1.0 : 13.8 or 1 : 14 (2 sig figs).

Question 9.1   In each case, it is best to start by writing down an unbalanced equation that shows just the reactants and products with their correct formulae.

(a) $Cu(s) + O_2(g) \longrightarrow CuO(s)$

There are two oxygen atoms on the left and only one on the right. Replacing CuO by 2CuO corrects this. Now there are two copper atoms on the right and only one on the left. Replacing Cu by 2Cu corrects that:

$$2Cu(s) + O_2(g) \longrightarrow 2CuO(s)$$

(b) $CO(g) + O_2(g) \longrightarrow CO_2(g)$

There are three oxygen atoms on the left and only two on the right. The oxygen atoms can be increased to four on each side if CO_2 is replaced by $2CO_2$, and CO by 2CO. Now the equation is also balanced in carbon atoms (there are two on each side):

$$2CO(g) + O_2(g) \longrightarrow 2CO_2(g)$$

(c) $NH_3(g) + CuO(s) \longrightarrow N_2(g) + H_2O(l) + Cu(s)$

Start by balancing the hydrogen atoms. The easiest way to equalize them is by replacing NH_3 by $2NH_3$, and H_2O by $3H_2O$. There are then six on each side:

$$2NH_3(g) + CuO(s) \longrightarrow N_2(g) + 3H_2O(l) + Cu(s)$$

Oxygen next: there are three atoms on the right and only one on the left. This is rectified by replacing CuO by 3CuO. Then the copper atoms can be balanced by replacing Cu by 3Cu:

$$2NH_3(g) + 3CuO(s) \longrightarrow N_2(g) + 3H_2O(l) + 3Cu(s)$$

(d) $C_3H_8(g) + O_2(g) \longrightarrow CO_2(g) + H_2O(g)$

Start as in the methane example with the carbon atoms, leaving oxygen until last. To match the three carbon atoms on the left, replace CO_2 by $3CO_2$ on the right:

$$C_3H_8(g) + O_2(g) \longrightarrow 3CO_2(g) + H_2O(g)$$

Hydrogen next: there are eight on the left and only two on the right. Correct this by replacing H_2O by $4H_2O$. Then to balance the 10 oxygen atoms on the right, replace O_2 by $5O_2$:

$$C_3H_8(g) + 5O_2(g) \longrightarrow 3CO_2(g) + 4H_2O(g)$$

Question 10.1

Step 1: since ammonia is 82.2% nitrogen and 17.8% hydrogen, in ammonia:

82.2 g of nitrogen are combined with 17.8 g of hydrogen

Step 2: it follows that

$$\text{1.00 g nitrogen is combined with } \frac{17.8\,g}{82.2} \text{ of hydrogen}$$

Now one mole of nitrogen atoms has a mass of 14.0 g, so

$$\text{14.0 g of nitrogen are combined with } \frac{17.8 \times 14.0\,g}{82.2}$$
of hydrogen

$$= 3.03 \text{ g hydrogen}$$

Step 3: one mole of hydrogen atoms has a mass of 1.01 g. It follows that 3.03 g of hydrogen contain $\frac{3.03\,g}{1.01\,g}$ or 3.00 moles of hydrogen atoms.

Step 4: since, in ammonia, every mole of nitrogen atoms is combined with three moles of hydrogen atoms, the chemical formula is NH_3. This is also the formula in Table 8.2.

Question 10.2   As in Question 9.1, start with the unbalanced equation:

$$H_2S(g) + SO_2(g) \longrightarrow H_2O(l) + S(s)$$

As sulfur appears on its own as S(s), we leave that till last. Oxygen is a good element with which to start the balancing act. There are two oxygen atoms on the left and only one on the right. Replacing H_2O by $2H_2O$ corrects this:

$$H_2S(g) + SO_2(g) \longrightarrow 2H_2O(l) + S(s)$$

Now there are only two hydrogen atoms on the left and four on the right. Replacing H_2S by $2H_2S$ corrects that:

$$2H_2S(g) + SO_2(g) \longrightarrow 2H_2O(l) + S(s)$$

Now we finish with sulfur atoms. Replacing S by 3S gives us three on each side, and the correctly balanced equation:

$$2H_2S(g) + SO_2(g) \longrightarrow 2H_2O(l) + 3S(s)$$

Question 10.3   (a) 14.0 g; (b) 14.0 g; (c) 24.0 g; (d) 117 g; (e) 154 g.

In each case you add up the relative atomic masses in the formula unit, multiply by the number of moles, and add the symbol for the gram. In the case of the two moles of NaCl in (d), for example, the relative atomic masses are Na = 23.0 and Cl = 35.5. So the sum of the relative atomic masses is (23.0 + 35.5) = 58.5. Multiplying by two and adding the symbol for the gram gives 117 g. Likewise in (e), the sum of the relative atomic masses is $[(3 \times 12.0) + (8 \times 1.01)] = 44.1$. Multiplying by 3.5, and adding the symbol for the gram gives 154 g. Note that one mole of N and 0.5 mole of N_2 are composed of identical masses of nitrogen. They both contain one zillion nitrogen atoms.

Question 10.4   The molecule of hydrogen chloride has the greater mass. The relative molecular masses are 17.0 for ammonia $[14.0 + (3 \times 1.01)]$, and 36.5 for hydrogen chloride (35.5 + 1.01).

Question 10.5   From the equation, two moles of H_2SO_4 are produced from two moles of sulfur atoms, S. So one mole of H_2SO_4 will be produced from one mole of S. Now we add up the relative atomic masses in these formula units. Using the relative atomic masses H = 1.01, S = 32.1 and O = 16.0, we find that one mole of H_2SO_4 has a mass of $[(2 \times 1.01) + 32.1 + (4 \times 16.0)]$ g or 98.1 g; one mole of S has a mass of 32.1 g. It follows that:

98.1 g of H_2SO_4 are produced from 32.1 g of sulfur

1.00 g of H_2SO_4 is produced from $\dfrac{32.1\,g}{98.1}$ of sulfur

2 500 g of H_2SO_4 are produced from $\dfrac{2\,500 \times 32.1\,g}{98.1}$ of sulfur

= 818 g of sulfur

As 2 500 g of H_2SO_4 are produced from 818 g of sulfur, 2 500 tonnes will be formed from 818 tonnes of sulfur.

Question 10.6   (a) The composition tells us that in aluminium bromide:

10.1 g of aluminium are combined with 89.9 g of bromine

1.00 g of aluminium is combined with $\dfrac{89.9\,g}{10.1}$ of bromine

1.00 mole of aluminium atoms, Al, has a mass of 27.0 g

1.00 mole of Al is combined with $\dfrac{27.0 \times 89.9\,g}{10.1}$ of bromine

= 240 g of bromine

One mole of bromine atoms, Br, has a mass of 79.9 g, so 240 g of bromine contain (240 g/79.9 g) or 3.00 moles of Br. Since, in aluminium bromide, every mole of Al is combined with three moles of Br, the empirical formula is $AlBr_3$.

(b) Since each bromine atom combines with one hydrogen atom in the hydride, the valency of bromine is one. As each aluminium atom combines with three bromine atoms, the valency of aluminium must then be three.

(c) The ratio of the density of the gaseous bromide to that of hydrogen, at STP, is $\frac{23.9}{0.0899} = 266$. Applying Equation 10.7 then gives 532 for the relative molecular mass of the gaseous bromide. This is double the relative molecular mass of an $AlBr_3$ unit (267). So the molecular formula of the gas is Al_2Br_6.

Question 10.7   (a) AlH_3; (b) Al_2O_3; (c) $AlCl_3$; (d) AlN. Apply point 12 of the summary in Section 10.8. For example, the valency of aluminium is three and that of oxygen is two, so in aluminium oxide, two atoms of aluminium will combine with three of oxygen. Note that for the nitride, this rule tells us that three atoms of aluminium combine with three atoms of nitrogen. So one atom of Al combines with one atom of N: the empirical formula is AlN.

Question 11.1

$$RbOH(aq) + HClO_4(aq) \longrightarrow RbClO_4(aq) + H_2O(l)$$

$$Ba(OH)_2(aq) + 2HClO_4(aq) \longrightarrow Ba(ClO_4)_2(aq) + 2H_2O(l)$$

In the first case, the single hydroxide group of RbOH must combine with a single hydrogen in $HClO_4$ to form water, and so the salt is $RbClO_4$. This is rubidium perchlorate, the -ate ending indicating the presence of oxygen in the acid group. In the second case, the two hydroxide groups in $Ba(OH)_2$ require *two* hydrogen atoms from *two* $HClO_4$ units to form water and so the salt is $Ba(ClO_4)_2$, barium perchlorate. In the formula $RbClO_4$ there are one rubidium, one chlorine and four oxygen atoms. In $Ba(ClO_4)_2$, all atoms within the brackets must be doubled: there are one barium, two chlorine and eight oxygen atoms.

Question 12.1 Z is antimony (Sb). The *highest* oxide, Z_2O_5, suggests (point 7c of Section 12.3) a Group V element, and point 7b confirms that these elements form a hydride ZH_3. The Group V element between rubidium and xenon is antimony: it lies in Period 5. Its highest fluoride should (point 7c) have the empirical formula SbF_5; and it does.

Question 13.1

(a) $NaI(s) \longrightarrow Na^+(aq) + I^-(aq)$

(b) $HClO_4(l) \longrightarrow H^+(aq) + ClO_4^-(aq)$

(c) $MgSO_4(s) \longrightarrow Mg^{2+}(aq) + SO_4^{2-}(aq)$

(d) $AlCl_3(s) \longrightarrow Al^{3+}(aq) + 3Cl^-(aq)$

(e) $Na_3PO_4(s) \longrightarrow 3Na^+(aq) + PO_4^{3-}(aq)$

(f) $K_2SO_4(s) \longrightarrow 2K^+(aq) + SO_4^{2-}(aq)$

(g) $NH_4NO_3(s) \longrightarrow NH_4^+(aq) + NO_3^-(aq)$

In each case, the formula of the dissolving substance is written down on the left. Then you can write down the appropriate number of H^+, Na^+, Cl^-, NO_3^- or SO_4^{2-} ions on the right. For example, for Na_3PO_4, there are three sodium atoms in the chemical formula, and these appear as $3Na^+(aq)$ on the right. When three sodiums are removed from an Na_3PO_4 unit, a PO_4 group remains. This must be added to the right-hand side as the ion $PO_4^{3-}(aq)$. It requires three negative charges to match the three positive charges of $3Na^+(aq)$. The name of the ion $PO_4^{3-}(aq)$ is the *phosphate ion*. The logic of the other examples is similar.

Question 13.2 Since the solution is conducting, $CuCl_2$ dissolved in water contains ions, and as there are two chlorine atoms in $CuCl_2$, two chloride or $Cl^-(aq)$ ions should be formed. The copper ion must therefore be $Cu^{2+}(aq)$, the double positive charge being needed to balance the two negative charges of $2Cl^-(aq)$:

$$CuCl_2(s) \longrightarrow Cu^{2+}(aq) + 2Cl^-(aq)$$

When the solution is electrolysed, the Cu^{2+} ions migrate to the negative electrode, where each takes up two electrons to form an atom of the red metallic film, which must be solid metallic copper:

$$Cu^{2+}(aq) + 2e^- \longrightarrow Cu(s)$$

At the same time, two chloride ions each surrender an electron at the positive electrode to give two chlorine atoms, which immediately pair to give a molecule of chlorine gas:

$$2Cl^-(aq) \longrightarrow Cl_2(g) + 2e^-$$

Two electrons have thereby been transferred across the gap between the electrodes.

Question 13.3 (a) The neutral aluminium atom contains equal numbers of positive and negative charges. To get the ion Al^{3+}, the positive charges must be in surplus by three. This requires the *removal* of three electrons.

(b) To get O^{2-} from O, the negative charges must get into surplus by two. This can be achieved by the *addition* of two electrons to the oxygen atom.

Question 14.1 There are nine protons, nine orbiting electrons and 10 neutrons. The preceding subscript is the atomic number, which takes the value 9. This is equal to the number of protons in the nucleus, and the number of electrons in the neutral atom. The preceding superscript is the mass number and takes the value 19. The number of neutrons is the mass number less the atomic number: $19 - 9 = 10$.

Question 14.2 (a) 13; (b) 13; (c) 14; (d) $^{27}_{13}Al$

Figure 12.7 shows that the serial number and atomic number of aluminium, Al, is 13, so there are 13 protons in the nucleus, and 13 orbiting electrons in the atom. As the relative atomic mass is 27.0, and there is just one isotope, the mass number is 27. Therefore the number of neutrons is $(27 - 13) = 14$. The mass number becomes the preceding superscript, and the atomic number the preceding subscript to the symbol in $^{27}_{13}Al$.

Question 14.3 (a) 92; (b) 143 and 146 respectively; (c) 238.

The number of protons is given by the atomic number, which is the preceding subscript and is 92 for both isotopes. All uranium isotopes contain 92 protons. The numbers of neutrons, 143 and 146, are obtained by subtracting the atomic number from the mass numbers, 235 and 238. As uranium is nearly all $^{238}_{92}U$, the relative atomic mass will be very close to the mass number of this isotope.

Question 14.4 (a) Pairs 2 and 3 are isotopes of the same element. In each pair, the atoms contain the same number of protons, and so have the same atomic number.

(b) See Table 14.2. The number of protons gives the atomic number, and this allows us to find the symbol in Figure 12.6. The mass number is the sum of the numbers of neutrons and protons.

Table 14.2 Answer to Question 14.4.

	First atom of pair	Second atom of pair
pair 1	$^{40}_{18}Ar$	$^{40}_{19}K$
pair 2	$^{36}_{18}Ar$	$^{38}_{18}Ar$
pair 3	$^{40}_{20}Ca$	$^{42}_{20}Ca$
pair 4	$^{239}_{94}Pu$	$^{235}_{90}Th$

Question 14.5 The isotopes that are produced alongside $^{4}_{2}He$ have mass numbers that are four less than those of the decaying isotopes $^{222}_{86}Rn$ and $^{238}_{92}U$, and atomic numbers that are two less. Their atomic numbers are therefore 84 and 90, respectively. From this, we deduce that they are isotopes of Po (polonium) and Th (thorium), and the equations are:

$$^{222}_{86}Rn \longrightarrow ^{218}_{84}Po + ^{4}_{2}He$$

$$^{238}_{92}U \longrightarrow ^{234}_{90}Th + ^{4}_{2}He$$

The names of the elements can be found from Appendix 1.

Question 14.6 (a) The relative atomic mass of oxygen is 16.0, so 32.0 g contain two moles of oxygen atoms. Two moles of oxygen atoms contain $2 \times 6.02 \times 10^{23}$, or 1.20×10^{24}, oxygen atoms.

(b) The relative molecular mass of O_2 is 32.0, so 32.0 g of oxygen contain one mole of O_2 molecules. This is 6.02×10^{23} oxygen molecules.

(c) The required relative atomic masses are Ca = 40.1 and O = 16.0, so one mole of CaO has a mass of (40.1 + 16.0) g or 56.1 g. Thus, 28.05 g are 0.500 mole, and contain $0.500 \times 6.02 \times 10^{23}$ formula units. This is 3.01×10^{23} formula units. Each formula unit, CaO, contains one calcium and one oxygen atom, so there are 3.01×10^{23} oxygen atoms and 3.01×10^{23} calcium atoms in 28.05 g of quicklime.

(d) The relative atomic mass of gold is 197, so one mole has a mass of 197 g. Therefore 1.97 g are 0.01 mole, and contain $0.01 \times 6.02 \times 10^{23}$ atoms. This is 6.02×10^{21} gold atoms.

(e) The required relative atomic masses are Na = 23.0 and S = 32.1, so one mole of Na_2S has a mass of $[(2 \times 23.0) + 32.1]$ g or 78.1 g. So 312.4 g of sodium sulfide contain $\frac{312.4}{78.1}$ or 4.00 moles of Na_2S. It therefore contains $4.00 \times 6.02 \times 10^{23}$, or 2.41×10^{24}, formula units of Na_2S. Each formula unit contains two sodium atoms and one sulfur atom. Therefore 312.4 g of sodium sulfide contains $2 \times 2.41 \times 10^{24}$ sodium atoms and 2.41×10^{24} sulfur atoms. This is 4.82×10^{24} sodium atoms and 2.41×10^{24} sulfur atoms.

(f) The required relative atomic masses are Al = 27.0 and O = 16.0, so one mole of Al_2O_3 has a mass of $[(2 \times 27.0) + (3 \times 16.0)]$ g or 102 g. So 153.0 g of aluminium oxide contain $\frac{153.0}{102}$ or 1.50 moles of Al_2O_3. This mass therefore contains $1.50 \times 6.02 \times 10^{23}$ or 9.03×10^{23} formula units of Al_2O_3. But each formula unit contains two aluminium atoms and three oxygen atoms. Therefore 153.0 g of aluminium oxide contain $2 \times 9.03 \times 10^{23}$ aluminium atoms and $3 \times 9.03 \times 10^{23}$ oxygen atoms. This is 1.81×10^{24} aluminium atoms and 2.71×10^{24} oxygen atoms.

Appendix 1 Relative atomic masses and atomic numbers of the elements

Relative atomic masses are given to three significant figures.

Element	Symbol	Atomic number	Relative atomic mass
actinium	Ac	89	227
aluminium	Al	13	27.0
americium	Am	95	243
antimony	Sb	51	122
argon	Ar	18	39.9
arsenic	As	33	74.9
astatine	At	85	210
barium	Ba	56	137
berkelium	Bk	97	247
beryllium	Be	4	9.01
bismuth	Bi	83	209
bohrium	Bh	107	264
boron	B	5	10.8
bromine	Br	35	79.9
cadmium	Cd	48	112
caesium	Cs	55	133
calcium	Ca	20	40.1
californium	Cf	98	251
carbon	C	6	12.0
cerium	Ce	58	140
chlorine	Cl	17	35.5
chromium	Cr	24	52.0
cobalt	Co	27	58.9
copper	Cu	29	63.5
curium	Cm	96	247
dubnium	Db	105	262
dysprosium	Dy	66	163
einsteinium	Es	99	252
erbium	Er	68	167
europium	Eu	63	152
fermium	Fm	100	257
fluorine	F	9	19.0
francium	Fr	87	223
gadolinium	Gd	64	157
gallium	Ga	31	69.7
germanium	Ge	32	72.6
gold	Au	79	197
hafnium	Hf	72	178
hassium	Hs	108	269
helium	He	2	4.00
holmium	Ho	67	165
hydrogen	H	1	1.01
indium	In	49	115
iodine	I	53	127
iridium	Ir	77	192
iron	Fe	26	55.8
krypton	Kr	36	83.8
lanthanum	La	57	139
lawrencium	Lr	103	262
lead	Pb	82	207
lithium	Li	3	6.94

Element	Symbol	Atomic number	Relative atomic mass
lutetium	Lu	71	175
magnesium	Mg	12	24.3
manganese	Mn	25	54.9
meitnerium	Mt	109	268
mendelevium	Md	101	258
mercury	Hg	80	201
molybdenum	Mo	42	95.9
neodymium	Nd	60	144
neon	Ne	10	20.2
neptunium	Np	93	237
nickel	Ni	28	58.7
niobium	Nb	41	92.9
nitrogen	N	7	14.0
nobelium	No	102	259
osmium	Os	76	190
oxygen	O	8	16.0
palladium	Pd	46	106
phosphorus	P	15	31.0
platinum	Pt	78	195
plutonium	Pu	94	244
polonium	Po	84	210
potassium	K	19	39.1
praseodymium	Pr	59	141
promethium	Pm	61	145
protactinium	Pa	91	231
radium	Ra	88	226
radon	Rn	86	222
rhenium	Re	75	186
rhodium	Rh	45	103
rubidium	Rb	37	85.5
ruthenium	Ru	44	101
rutherfordium	Rf	104	261
samarium	Sm	62	150
scandium	Sc	21	45.0
seaborgium	Sg	106	266
selenium	Se	34	79.0
silicon	Si	14	28.1
silver	Ag	47	108
sodium	Na	11	23.0
strontium	Sr	38	87.6
sulfur	S	16	32.1
tantalum	Ta	73	181
technetium	Tc	43	98.0
tellurium	Te	52	128
terbium	Tb	65	159
thallium	Tl	81	204
thorium	Th	90	232
thulium	Tm	69	169
tin	Sn	50	119
titanium	Ti	22	47.9
tungsten	W	74	184
uranium	U	92	238
vanadium	V	23	50.9
xenon	Xe	54	131
ytterbium	Yb	70	173
yttrium	Y	39	88.9
zinc	Zn	30	65.4
zirconium	Zr	40	91.2

Acknowledgements

Grateful acknowledgement is made to the following sources for permission to reproduce material in this block:

Figures

Figures 1.1 and 15.1: courtesy of IBM Corporation, Research Division, Almaden Research Center; *Figure 2.2*: Dorset Natural History and Archaeological Society; *Figures 2.3, 2.12 and 6.4:* courtesy of A. G. Tindle; *Figure 2.4*: The Natural History Museum, London; *Figure 2.8*: *Times Atlas of the World*, © Times 1978. Reproduced with permission of HarperCollins Cartographic. MM-1097-52; *Figure 2.20*: © Camera Press; *Figure 3.1*: courtesy of Sartorius Ltd; *Figure 3.5*: The Ferdinand Hamburger Jr. Archives of The Johns Hopkins University; *Figure 3.6*: courtesy of D. R. Roberts; *Figures 4.2, 6.1 and 8.2*: Reproduced courtesy of the Library and Information Centre of the Royal Society of Chemistry; *Figure 6.2*: © David Smith; *Figure 6.7*: courtesy of British Gas; *Figure 6.8*: courtesy of Paul Doherty; *Figure 7.2*: photo by Robert W Madden, © National Geographical Society; *Figure 7.4*: courtesy of J. Allan Cash Ltd; *Figures 7.18, 10.4, 12.2, 12.3, 14.2 and 14.7*: Science Museum/ Science and Society Picture Library; *Figure 9.1*: NASA /BARA-King; *Figure 10.5*: courtesy of Johnson Matthey; *Figure 10.6*: British Museum; *Figure 10.8*: From Vincent, W. T. *Records of the Woolwich District*, volume 2 (1890); *Figure 11.2*: Hulton Getty Picture Collection; *Figure 11.3*: from *Murder America* 1987, Harrap UK, HarperCollins Publishers Ltd; *Figure 12.1*: Ann Ronan/Image Select; *Figure 14.5*: courtesy of the National Radiological Protection Board; *Figure 14.17a*: courtesy of Topometrix Corporation.

Index

Entries and page numbers in **bold type** refer to key words which are printed in **bold** in the text and which are defined in the Glossary. These are terms that we expect you to be able to explain the meaning of, and use correctly, both during and at the end of the course. An entry followed by^G indicates a term which is defined in the Glossary but which is not bold in the text. Where the page number is given in *italics*, the indexed information is carried mainly or wholly in an illustration or table. Section summaries and answers to questions are not indexed.

S103 Course Team

S103 *Discovering Science* was produced for the Science Faculty by a team drawn from many areas of the Open University. The full list of contributors to the course is printed in the S103 *Course Guide*.

Block 6 was produced for the S103 Course Team by the team of people listed below.

Block Chair and author:	David Johnson (Chemistry)
Course Team Chair:	Stuart Freake
Course Manager:	Isla McTaggart
Editor:	Dick Sharp
OU Graphic Design:	Ruth Drage, Alison George, John Taylor
Centre for Educational Software	Philip Butcher, Chris Denham, Fiona Thomson
BBC/OUPC (video production):	David Jackson
External course assessor:	Prof. Paul Black (King's College, London)
External block assessor:	Dr P.G. Nelson (University of Hull)

The block has also benefited greatly from comments and other forms of help during its production from Audrey Brown (Associate Lecturer), David Campbell (AL), Norman Cohen, Nancy Dise, Gillian Eastmond (AL), Bob Hill (AL), Sally Jordan (AL), Clive Lawless (IET), Mike Mortimer, David Roberts, Canan Tosunglu Blake (IET), Helen Wood (AL) and all the students who tested materials.